Introduction to
p-Adic Numbers and
Valuation Theory

ACADEMIC PAPERBACKS*

BIOLOGY

Edited by ALVIN NASON

Design and Function at the Threshold of Life: The Viruses
HEINZ FRAENKEL-CONRAT
Time, Cells, and Aging BERNARD L. STREHLER
Isotopes in Biology GEORGE WOLF
Life: Its Nature, Origin, and Development A. I. OPARIN

MATHEMATICS

Edited by W. MAGNUS and A. SHENITZER

Finite Permutation Groups HELMUT WIELANDT
Introduction to p-Adic Numbers and Valuation Theory
GEORGE BACHMAN
Quadratic Forms and Matrices N. V. YEFIMOV
Elements of Abstract Harmonic Analysis
GEORGE BACHMAN
Noneuclidean Geometry HERBERT MESCHKOWSKI

PHYSICS

Edited by D. ALLAN BROMLEY

Elementary Dynamics of Particles H. W. HARKNESS
Elementary Plane Rigid Dynamics H. W. HARKNESS
Crystals: Their Role in Nature and in Science CHARLES BUNN
Potential Barriers in Semiconductors B. R. GOSSICK
Mössbauer Effect: Principles and Applications
GUNTHER K. WERTHEIM

* Most of these volumes are also available in a cloth bound edition.

Introduction to
p-Adic Numbers
and
Valuation Theory

By George Bachman

POLYTECHNIC INSTITUTE OF BROOKLYN
MATHEMATICS DEPARTMENT
BROOKLYN, NEW YORK

ACADEMIC PRESS · New York and London

ACADEMIC PRESS INC.
111 Fifth Avenue, New York, New York 10003

United Kingdom Edition published by
ACADEMIC PRESS INC. (LONDON) LTD.
Berkeley Square House, London W.1

LIBRARY OF CONGRESS CATALOG CARD NUMBER: 64-17793

PRINTED IN THE UNITED STATES OF AMERICA

Preface

The field of p-adic numbers, which can be obtained from the field of rational numbers by a completion process with respect to a special kind of mapping, or valuation, similar in many respects to the ordinary absolute value mapping has a great number of interesting properties. However, beyond this, it turns out that such fields are of particular interest and importance in algebraic number theory and in algebraic geometry. This is equally true of the general notion of a valuation together with some of its related concepts.

The book is meant to serve as an introduction to valuation theory. The first two chapters have been written mainly for advanced undergraduate students and first year graduate students. The amount of algebra required is quite small, and the algebraic results needed for these two chapters are included in the first four sections of the appendix. It is hoped that in this fashion these two chapters will be reasonably self-contained and available to as wide an audience as possible. In addition, exercises have been added to these chapters most of which are intended to give the reader some manipulative facility with the concepts introduced.

The remaining three chapters definitely demand more mathematical maturity on the part of the reader. At least a first course in modern algebra would be required to read parts of them. Although most of the material needed for these chapters has been stated in the appendix, this is meant just to serve as a handy glossary for the reader. References have been supplied for this material.

It is hoped that the treatment of the material throughout the book itself will prove to be leisurely. We have been somewhat repetitious in places in the hope of gaining increased clarity. Again, the most elegant proofs of some theorems have not been used when it was felt that other proofs were clearer. The development of certain sections is based to a large extent on lectures given by E. Artin. In particular, Sections 1, 2, 4, and 5 of

Chapter III are based on lecture notes written by the author for
a course given in algebraic geometry at N.Y.U. by Professor
Artin (see [3] in bibliography). Needless to say, the author
assumes all responsibility for the proofs presented.

In a short introductory treatment of this sort, there was no
opportunity to present the many beautiful applications of the
subject matter to such areas as algebraic number theory or
algebraic geometry. Although some hints of the applications to
number theory are given. In the bibliography, a number of
books which treat the applications have been listed along with
texts and periodical literature which go deeper into the subject
matter itself, and, finally, some books relevant to the material
listed in the appendix have been added. No attempt has been
made for anything resembling a complete bibliography.

We follow the customary abbreviations by writing, for example,
II, (1.3) in referring to Chapter II, Section 1, Equation (1.3).
In referring to the appendix, we write, for example, A,2 meaning
Section 2 of the appendix. Numbers occurring in brackets refer
to the bibliography.

The author would like finally to express his appreciation to
Professor W. Magnus for his encouragement and advice throughout the writing of this book. He would also like to express his
gratitude to Mr. Lawrence Narici for his helpful suggestions in
the preparation of the manuscript.

G. BACHMAN

Brooklyn, New York

Contents

PREFACE   v

SYMBOLS USED IN TEXT   ix

Chapter I Valuations of Rank One

1. p-Adic Valuations of Q   1
2. Definition of a Valuation of Rank 1   4
3. Equivalent Valuations   16
    Exercises   23

Chapter II Complete Fields and the Field of p-Adic Numbers

1. Completion of a Field with Respect to a
    Valuation   24
2. p-Adic Numbers   33
3. Some Analysis in Q_p   43
4. Newton's Method in Complete Fields   52
5. Roots of Unity in Q_p   61
    Exercises   63

Chapter III Valuation Rings, Places, and Valuations

1. Valuation Rings and Places   65
2. Valuations   70
3. Valuations of General Rank   76
4. The Extension Theorem   83
5. Integral Closure   88

Chapter IV Normed Linear Spaces

1. Basic Properties of Normed Linear Spaces   92
2. Linear Functionals   99
3. Banach Algebras   110

Chapter V Extensions of Valuations

1. The Extension Problem 117
2. The Number of Extensions of a Valuation 128
3. Valuations of Algebraic Number Fields—
   Examples 137
4. Discrete Valuations 142

Appendix

1. Sets and Mappings 153
2. Number Theory 155
3. Groups 158
4. Rings, Ideals, and Fields 161
5. Glossary for Rings and Fields 164
6. Adèles and Idèles 167

BIBLIOGRAPHY 168

SUBJECT INDEX 171

Symbols Used in Text

The chapter, section, and page on which they are first introduced are listed.

Z	Set of all integers, I, 1, p. 1.
Q	Set of all rational numbers, I, 1, p. 1.
R	Set of all real numbers, I, 1, p. 1.
C	Set of all complex numbers, I, 1, p. 1.
$\|\|_p$	p-Adic valuation of Q, I, 1, p. 2.
d	Distance function, I, 1, p. 3, and IV, 1, p. 93.
$v(a) = -\log\| a \|$,	I, 2, p. 5.
$\|\|_1 \sim \|\|_2$	Equivalent valuations, I, 3, p. 16.
$\hat{k}$	Completion of a field k, II, 1, p. 26.
Q_p	p-Adic numbers, II, 2, p. 34.
$\text{ord}_p\, x$	Ordinal of x at p, II, 3, p. 45.
$\text{ord}\, x$	Ordinal of x, V, 4, p. 143.
$a < b$	In an order group, III, 2, p. 71.
$K^* = K - \{0\}$	Multiplicative group of the field K, III, 2, p. 73.
$\|\ \|$	Norm mapping, IV, 1, p. 92.
$\|\ \|_1 \sim \|\ \|_2$	Equivalent norms, IV, 1, p. 94.
$\|\ \|_0$	0-Norm on a finite-dimensional vector space, IV, 1, p. 95.
$\|f\|$	Norm of a bounded linear functional, IV, 2, p. 101.
$\sigma(x)$	Spectrum of x in a Banach algebra, IV, 3, p. 113.
$N_{K/k}(x)$	Norm from K to k, V, 1, p. 118 (A, 166).
e	Ramification index, V, 1, p. 121.
f	Residue class degree, V, 1, p. 121.

CHAPTER I

Valuations of Rank One

1. p-Adic Valuations of Q

In this chapter we wish to give a provisional definition of a valuation, or, more accurately, we wish to define a valuation of rank one. In Chapter III, this concept will be generalized. Throughout the text, we shall use the following notations: Z, the ring of integers; Q, the field of rational numbers; R, the field of real numbers; and C, the field of complex numbers.

Before giving the definition of a rank one valuation, we wish to motivate the definition by considering an example. Our aim is to extend the notion of the ordinary absolute value function on the field Q. We recall that the basic properties of this function, $|\ |: Q \rightarrow R$, are the following:

$$\text{for } x \in Q, \quad |x| \geqslant 0 \text{ and } = 0 \quad \text{if and only if} \quad x = 0; \quad (1.1)$$

$$\text{for } x, y \in Q, \quad |xy| = |x||y|; \quad (1.2)$$

$$\text{(the triangle inequality)} \quad |x + y| \leqslant |x| + |y|. \quad (1.3)$$

We shall now construct other mappings of Q into R which satisfy these conditions. Actually these functions will satisfy a much stronger condition than (1.3). Instead of "weighing" the rational number x according to its numerical value $|x|$, we shall now "weigh" it in a certain sense according to the presence of a fixed prime, p. We now proceed more precisely in constructing these functions.

Let $c \in R$, where $0 < c < 1$; c will be fixed throughout the discussion. Also, let p be a fixed prime number. If x is any rational number other than 0, we can write x in the form

$$x = p^\alpha \frac{a}{b}.$$

where a, $b \in Z$, $p \nmid a$, and $p \nmid b$, and where $\alpha \in Z$. Clearly, α may be positive, negative, or zero depending on x. We now define

$$| x |_p = c^\alpha, \quad \text{and} \quad | 0 |_p = 0.$$

It follows immediately from the definition that $| x |_p \geqslant 0$ and equals 0 if and only if $x = 0$. Furthermore, if $y = p^\beta(a'/b')$, where $p \nmid a'$ and $p \nmid b'$, then

$$xy = p^{\alpha+\beta} \frac{aa'}{bb'},$$

where $p \nmid bb'$ and $p \nmid aa'$. Hence,

$$| xy |_p = c^{\alpha+\beta} = | x |_p | y |_p.$$

Finally, we shall show that

$$| x + y |_p \leqslant \max (| x |_p, | y |_p). \tag{1.4}$$

It is clear that (1.4) is a much stronger statement than (1.3), i.e., from (1.4) it follows immediately that the function $| \ |_p$ satisfies condition (1.3). Instead of proving (1.4), we shall prove the following equivalent condition:

$$| x |_p \leqslant 1 \Rightarrow | 1 + x |_p \leqslant 1. \tag{1.5}$$

We first note that (1.4) is, indeed, equivalent to (1.5), for, suppose (1.4) is satisfied, then, if $| x |_p \leqslant 1$,

$$| 1 + x |_p \leqslant \max (| x |_p, 1) = 1,$$

and (1.5) holds. Conversely, suppose (1.5) is true. We may assume that $y \neq 0$, for, if $y = 0$, (1.4) is trivially true. Also, we may assume without loss of generality that $| x |_p \leqslant | y |_p$. Then $| x/y |_p \leqslant 1$ and, therefore, by (1.5)

$$\left| 1 + \frac{x}{y} \right|_p \leqslant 1, \quad \text{so} \quad | x + y |_p \leqslant | y |_p = \max (| x |_p, | y |_p).$$

Thus, we must just show that (1.5) is true. It follows immediately from the definition of $| x |_p$ for $x \neq 0$ that if $| x |_p \leqslant 1$, then

$\alpha \geqslant 0$, and x can be written in the form $x = c/d$, where $(c, d) = 1$, and $p \nmid d$. Then

$$1 + x = 1 + \frac{c}{d} = \frac{c + d}{d},$$

and $1 + x$ also has a denominator prime to p; whence, $\mid 1 + x \mid_p \leqslant 1$. Since (1.5) holds trivially if $x = 0$, the proof is completed.

We have, therefore, shown that the function $\mid \;\mid_p$ satisfies all the conditions that the ordinary absolute value function satisfies, and, moreover, $\mid \;\mid_p$ satisfies condition (1.4), which is certainly not true for $\mid \;\mid$. We wish to make some further observations concerning this function. Define in terms of the function $\mid \;\mid_p$ a new function,

$$d: \quad Q \times Q \to R,$$

namely,

$$d(x, y) = \mid x - y \mid_p . \tag{1.6}$$

Let us see what properties the function d possesses. Clearly

$$d(x, y) \geqslant 0 \quad \text{and} \quad = 0 \quad \text{if and only if} \quad x = y. \tag{1.7}$$

$$d(y, x) = \mid y - x \mid_p = \mid -1 \mid_p \mid x - y \mid_p = \mid x - y \mid_p = d(x, y),$$

so

$$d(y, x) = d(x, y). \tag{1.8}$$

Finally,

$$\begin{aligned}
d(x, z) = \mid x - z \mid_p &= \mid (x - y) + (y - z) \mid_p \\
&\leqslant \max (\mid x - y \mid_p , \mid y - z \mid_p) \\
&= \max (d(x, y), d(y, z)).
\end{aligned}$$

Thus,

$$d(x, z) \leqslant \max (d(x, y), d(y, z)). \tag{1.9}$$

From (1.9), it follows immediately that

$$d(x, z) \leqslant d(x, y) + d(y, z). \tag{1.10}$$

A set X together with a function, $d: X \times X \to R$, which satisfies the conditions (1.7), (1.8), and (1.10) is called a *metric space*. Hence, Q together with the function $d(x, y) = |x - y|_p$ is a metric space, which actually satisfies the stronger condition (1.9). Equation (1.9) is frequently called the *ultrametric* inequality.

In a metric space, X, one can introduce the notion of convergence of a sequence of elements. There are a number of equivalent ways of introducing this concept, but the following will suffice for our purposes. The sequence $\{x_n\}$ in the metric space X is said to *converge* to the element $x \in X$, written $x_n \to x$, if and only if $d(x, x_n) \to 0$, as $n \to \infty$.

Let us now observe that in the metric space Q introduced above, the sequence

$$p, \quad p^2, ..., p^n, ...$$

converges to 0; namely,

$$d(0, p^n) = |p^n|_p = c^n,$$

and, since $0 < c < 1$, $c^n \to 0$ as $n \to \infty$.

At first sight, this might seem strange, but when one recalls that the distance function was defined in a manner entirely differently from the customary absolute value, this behavior of the sequence $\{p^n\}$ should not seem too surprising.

It is not difficult to show (see Exercise 1, page 23) that if X is a metric space in which the distance function d satisfies the ultrametric inequality, then, if $d(x, y) \neq d(y, z)$,

$$d(x, z) = \max (d(x, y), d(y, z)).$$

This result has the following geometric interpretation: every triangle in such a metric space is isosceles, and its base has length less than or equal to that of the equal sides.

2. Definition of a Valuation of Rank 1

We shall now extend the concept of the absolute value function on the field Q; namely:

Definition 2.1.   A valuation of rank 1 of a field k is a mapping, $|\ |$, from k into R such that for all $a, b \in k$

$$|a| \geqslant 0 \quad \text{and} \quad =0 \quad \text{if and only if} \quad a = 0; \quad (2.1)$$

$$|ab| = |a||b|; \quad (2.2)$$

$$|a+b| \leqslant |a| + |b|. \quad (2.3)$$

We shall generally omit the expression "of rank 1" in the first two chapters, and simply speak of such a function as a valuation, it being understood that such a map is always into R.

If the valuation satisfies, in addition, the condition

$$|a+b| \leqslant \max(|a|, |b|) \quad (2.4)$$

then it will be called a *non-archimedian valuation*. From the results obtained in Section 1, we see that the function $|\ |_p$ is a non-archimedian valuation of Q. We shall shortly see that there are essentially no other non-archimedian valuations of Q except for a trivial one. The valuation $|\ |_p$ is called the *p-adic valuation* of Q.

Before discussing various results which follow from the definition of a valuation, we shall reformulate the definition of a non-archimedian valuation. For $a \in k$, and $a \neq 0$, we define the function $v(a)$ as follows:

$$v(a) = -\log|a|, \quad (2.5)$$

while

$$v(0) = \infty,$$

where we have introduced the symbol ∞ and shall operate with it in the customary formal fashion. Thus, v is a mapping of k into the extended real number system, i.e., $v(a) \in R \cup \{\infty\}$, and $v(a) = \infty$ if and only if $a = 0$. Let us see what further conditions v satisfies. Since $|ab| = |a||b|$, we get

$$\log|ab| = \log|a||b| = \log|a| + \log|b|,$$
$$-\log|ab| = -\log|a| - \log|b|.$$

This, together with the rules for operating with ∞, gives

$$v(ab) = v(a) + v(b). \quad (2.6)$$

Also, since $| a + b | \leqslant \max (| a |, | b |)$,

$$\log | a + b | \leqslant \max (\log | a |, \log | b |),$$

and

$$-\log | a + b | \geqslant -\max (\log | a |, \log | b |),$$

i.e.,

$$-\log | a + b | \geqslant \min (-\log | a |, -\log | b |),$$

and we have

$$v(a + b) \geqslant \min (v(a), v(b)). \tag{2.7}$$

Thus, the function v satisfies the conditions (2.6) and (2.7) analogous to the conditions (2.2) and (2.4) for the non-archimedian valuation $| \ |$.

The following fact, which we formalize as a theorem is frequently useful—particularly in the consideration of examples.

Theorem 2.1.   Suppose $| \ |_1$ is a mapping of an integral domain A into R which satisfies the conditions (2.1) to (2.3). Then $| \ |_1$ can be extended uniquely to a valuation, $| \ |$, of the quotient field k.

   Proof.   If there exists a valuation $| \ |$ on k extending $| \ |_1$, then it is clear that for $x \in k$, where $x = a/b$, $a, b \in A$, we must have

$$| x | = \frac{| a |}{| b |} = \frac{| a |_1}{| b |_1}. \tag{2.8}$$

Thus we have uniqueness. Now let us show that (2.8), indeed, defines an extension $| \ |$ of $| \ |_1$ which is a valuation. We must first of all show that $| \ |$ is well defined. Thus, suppose $a/b = c/d$, then

$$ad = bc, \quad \text{and} \quad | ad |_1 = | bc |_1 ,$$

or

$$| a |_1 | d |_1 = | b |_1 | c |_1 , \qquad \frac{| a |_1}{| b |_1} = \frac{| c |_1}{| d |_1}.$$

Now we show that $|\ |$ satisfies the conditions for a valuation. Condition (2.1) is clear as is (2.2). If $y = c/d$, c, $d \in A$, then

$$x + y = \frac{ad + bc}{bd},$$

and

$$
\begin{aligned}
|\, x + y \,| = \frac{|\, ad + bc \,|_1}{|\, bd \,|_1} &\leqslant \frac{|\, ad \,|_1}{|\, bd \,|_1} + \frac{|\, bc \,|_1}{|\, bd \,|_1} \\
&= \frac{|\, a \,|_1}{|\, b \,|_1} + \frac{|\, c \,|_1}{|\, d \,|_1} \\
&= |\, x \,| + |\, y \,|.
\end{aligned}
$$

Finally, it is clear that $|\ |$ extends $|\ |_1$ for if $a \in A$, then $a = ab/b$, where $b \in A$, and

$$|\, a \,| = \frac{|\, ab \,|_1}{|\, b \,|_1} = \frac{|\, a \,|_1 |\, b \,|_1}{|\, b \,|_1} = |\, a \,|_1,$$

which completes the proof.

It follows immediately from Definition 2.1 that a valuation $|\ |$ satisfies the following conditions

$$|\, 1 \,| = 1 \tag{2.9}$$

$$|\, -1 \,| = 1 \tag{2.10}$$

$$\left|\, \frac{a}{b} \,\right| = \frac{|\, a \,|}{|\, b \,|} \tag{2.11}$$

$$\big|\, |\, a \,| - |\, b \,| \,\big| \leqslant |\, a - b \,|. \tag{2.12}$$

Let us now see what the counterpart of (2.12) is for a non-archimedian valuation. Thus, suppose $|\ |$ is non-archimedian, and suppose $|\, a \,| > |\, b \,|$. Then

$$|\, a \,| = |\, (a + b) - b \,| \leqslant \max(|\, a + b \,|, |\, b \,|).$$

Clearly $|\, a + b \,|$ must be the maximum, for, otherwise, we would have $|\, a \,| \leqslant |\, b \,|$, which contradicts our assumption. Hence,

$$|\, a \,| \leqslant |\, a + b \,| \leqslant \max(|\, a \,|, |\, b \,|) = |\, a \,|.$$

We, therefore, have:

Theorem 2.2. If $| \ |$ is a non-archimedian valuation, and if $|\,a\,| > |\,b\,|$, then $|\,a + b\,| = |\,a\,|$.

It is easily seen, by taking $a = -b$, that the theorem is not true if $|\,a\,| = |\,b\,|$. It also follows readily that, for a non-archimedian valuation,

$$|\,a_1 + a_2 + \cdots + a_n\,| \leqslant \max\,(|\,a_1\,|, |\,a_2\,|, ..., |\,a_n\,|),$$

and

$$|\,a_1 + a_2 + \cdots + a_n\,| = |\,a_1\,| \qquad \text{if} \qquad |\,a_j\,| < |\,a_1\,|$$
$$\text{for} \qquad j = 2, ..., n.$$

We continue to assume that $| \ |$ is a non-archimedian valuation, and we consider the set V of all $a \in k$ such that $|\,a\,| \leqslant 1$. If a, $b \in V$, then

$$|\,ab\,| = |\,a\,|\,|\,b\,| \leqslant 1,$$

and, therefore, $ab \in V$. Also,

$$|\,a - b\,| \leqslant \max\,(|\,a\,|, |\,b\,|) \leqslant 1.$$

Hence, V is a ring; also $1 \in V$.

Next, we consider P, which is the set of all $a \in k$ such that $|\,a\,| < 1$. Clearly, if a, $b \in P$, then $a + b \in P$, and if $a \in P$ and $b \in V$, then

$$|\,ba\,| = |\,b\,|\,|\,a\,| < 1,$$

so $ba \in P$. Therefore, P is an ideal in V. Moreover, if $a \in V$ and if $a \notin P$, then $|\,a\,| = 1$. Therefore, $|\,a^{-1}\,| = 1$. It follows that P is the unique maximal ideal of V, and, since $1 \in V$, that P is also a prime ideal. Summarizing, we have:

Theorem 2.3. If $| \ |$ is a non-archimedian valuation, then the set $V \subset k$ of all elements a such that $|\,a\,| \leqslant 1$ is a ring with identity. The set P of all elements a such that $|\,a\,| < 1$ is the unique maximal ideal of V, and P is also a prime ideal.

The ring V is called the *valuation ring* associated with the non-archimedian valuation $|\;|$. The field V/P is called the associated *residue class field*.

We have already obtained a number of valuations of Q, namely, the p-adic valuations as well as the usual absolute value. In addition, there is, of course, the *trivial valuation* which one can define for any field k, namely, $|\,0\,| = 0$ and $|\,a\,| = 1$ for all $a \neq 0$, $a \in k$. We wish to show that these exhaust all possible valuations of Q in a certain sense; that is, we set forth the problem: to find all valuations of Q. Before embarking on this project, we establish the following lemmas which will be needed in the course of our investigation.

Lemma 2.1. If $0 < r \leqslant s$, and if a_i, $i = 1, ..., n$ are non-negative real numbers, then

$$\Big(\sum_{i=1}^{n} a_i{}^s\Big)^{1/s} \leqslant \Big(\sum_{i=1}^{n} a_i{}^r\Big)^{1/r}.$$

Proof. Let $d = \sum_{i=1}^{n} a_i{}^r$. Then

$$\frac{(\sum_{i=1}^{n} a_i{}^s)^{1/s}}{d^{1/r}} = \Big(\sum_{i=1}^{n} \frac{a_i{}^s}{d^{s/r}}\Big)^{1/s}$$

$$= \Big(\sum_{i=1}^{n} \Big(\frac{a_i{}^r}{d}\Big)^{s/r}\Big)^{1/s}$$

$$\leqslant \Big(\sum_{i=1}^{n} \frac{a_i{}^r}{d}\Big)^{1/s}$$

since $a_i{}^r/d \leqslant 1$, and since $r \leqslant s$. But

$$\sum_{i=1}^{n} \frac{a_i{}^r}{d} = \frac{1}{d} \sum_{i=1}^{n} a_i{}^r = 1.$$

Therefore,

$$\Big(\sum_{i=1}^{n} a_i{}^s\Big)^{1/s} \leqslant d^{1/r} = \Big(\sum_{i=1}^{n} a_i{}^r\Big)^{1/r}.$$

Lemma 2.2. If $0 < \alpha \leqslant 1$, and if b_i, $i = 1, ..., n$ are non-negative real numbers, then

$$(b_1 + b_2 + \cdots + b_n)^\alpha \leqslant b_1{}^\alpha + b_2{}^\alpha + \cdots + b_n{}^\alpha. \quad (2.13)$$

Proof. In Lemma 2.1, choose $a_i = b_i$, $i = 1, ..., n$, $s = 1$ and $r = \alpha$. Then we obtain

$$b_1 + b_2 + \cdots + b_n \leqslant (b_1{}^\alpha + b_2{}^\alpha + \cdots + b_n{}^\alpha)^{1/\alpha},$$

or

$$(b_1 + b_2 + \cdots + b_n)^\alpha \leqslant b_1{}^\alpha + b_2{}^\alpha + \cdots + b_n{}^\alpha.$$

Now, we return to the problem at hand. Let m and n be two integers >1, and write m using the base n. Then

$$m = a_0 + a_1 n + a_2 n^2 + \cdots + a_k n^k,$$

where $0 \leqslant a_i \leqslant n - 1$, $i = 0, 1, ..., k$. Clearly, $n^k \leqslant m$. Hence,

$$k \leqslant \frac{\log m}{\log n}.$$

Assume now that $|\ |$ is a valuation of Q. Then applying (2.3), we have

$$|a_i| = |1 + 1 + \cdots + 1| \leqslant n.$$

Thus,

$$\begin{aligned}
|m| &\leqslant |a_0| + |a_1|\,|n| + |a_2|\,|n|^2 + \cdots + |a_k|\,|n|^k \\
&\leqslant n(1 + |n| + |n|^2 + \cdots + |n|^k) \\
&\leqslant n(k + 1) \max (1, |n|)^k.
\end{aligned}$$

Using the estimate on k, we, therefore, have

$$|m| \leqslant n \left(\frac{\log m}{\log n} + 1 \right) \max (1, |n|)^{\log m / \log n}, \quad (2.14)$$

which is true for any m, $n > 1$. Hence, replacing m by m^τ in (2.14), and then taking the τth root of both sides, we get

$$|m| \leqslant \sqrt[\tau]{n \left(\frac{\tau \log m}{\log n} + 1 \right)} \max (1, |n|)^{\log m / \log n}.$$

Finally, if we let $\tau \to \infty$ and use the fact that $\lim_{\tau \to \infty} \sqrt[\tau]{\tau} = 1$, then

$$|m| \leqslant \max(1, |n|)^{\log m / \log n}. \qquad (2.15)$$

There are now two distinct possibilities which we have to consider. The first is that there exists an $n > 1$ such that $|n| \leqslant 1$. Equation (2.15) then yields that $|m| \leqslant 1$ for all $m > 1$. From which it follows, using the fact that $|-1| = 1$, that $|m| \leqslant 1$ for all $m \in Z$. In this case, we show that the valuation, $|\ |$, must satisfy the stronger inequality (2.4). Actually, we can prove a stronger statement, and, because of its importance, we single this out as a theorem.

Theorem 2.4. Suppose k is a field with a valuation, $|\ |$, and suppose $|m| \leqslant d$ for all integers m of k (here the set of integers refers to the isomorphic image of Z if k has characteristic 0, or to the isomorphic image of the residue classes modulo p if k has characteristic p). Then the valuation, $|\ |$, is non-archimedian.

Proof.

$$|a + b|^\tau = |(a + b)^\tau|$$

$$= \left| a^\tau + \binom{\tau}{1} a^{\tau-1}b + \binom{\tau}{2} a^{\tau-2}b^2 + \cdots + b^\tau \right|$$

$$\leqslant |a|^\tau + \left| \binom{\tau}{1} \right| |a|^{\tau-1}|b| + \cdots + |b|^\tau$$

$$\leqslant (\tau + 1)d \max(|a|, |b|)^\tau.$$

Taking the τth root of both sides and letting $\tau \to \infty$, we obtain

$$|a + b| \leqslant \max(|a|, |b|),$$

which completes the proof.

Thus in our special case of a valuation $|\ |$ on Q under the first possibility, we obtain that $|\ |$ is non-archimedian.

If $|m| = 1$ for all $m \in Z$, $m \neq 0$, then using Theorem 2.1, we see that $|\ |$ is just the trivial valuation. Thus, let us suppose that

$|\,m\,| < 1$ occurs for some $m > 1$. Then let p be the smallest positive integer such that $|\,p\,| < 1$. We claim that p is a prime, for if $p = ab$, where $a, b < p$, and where a and b are positive, then

$$|\,p\,| = |\,a\,|\,|\,b\,| = 1,$$

which is a contradiction. Hence, p is a prime. Suppose $|\,m\,| < 1$. Then

$$m = qp + r, \qquad \text{where} \qquad 0 \leqslant r < p.$$

If $r \neq 0$, then, since $r < p$, we have $|\,r\,| = 1$. But

$$|\,qp\,| = |\,p + p + \cdots + p\,| \leqslant |\,p\,| < 1,$$

so $|\,m\,| = 1$, which is a contradiction. Thus, $p \mid m$, and, conversely, if $p \mid m$, then clearly $|\,m\,| < 1$.

Now if $x \in Q$, $x \neq 0$, then x has the form

$$x = p^{\alpha} \frac{a}{b},$$

where $p \nmid a$ and $p \nmid b$, and, therefore, by the immediately preceding discussion, we have

$$|\,x\,| = |\,p\,|^{\alpha} = c^{\alpha},$$

where $c = |\,p\,|$ is some real number such that $0 < c < 1$. Thus, in this case, $|\ |$ is a p-adic valuation. We have seen in Section 1 that all such functions are, indeed, valuations (non-archimedian) of Q.

Now let us consider the second possibility, namely, for any $n > 1$, $|\,n\,| > 1$. It follows from (2.15) that

$$|\,m\,|^{1/\log m} \leqslant |\,n\,|^{1/\log n},$$

and, since this is true for all $m, n > 1$, we get, interchanging m and n, the inequality in the opposite direction. Hence,

$$|\,m\,|^{1/\log m} = |\,n\,|^{1/\log n}; \qquad \text{that is,} \qquad |\,m\,|^{1/\log m} = c,$$

where c is independent of m. We observe that $c > 1$, and, therefore, we can write $c = e^{\alpha}$, where $\alpha > 0$. Then

$$|\,m\,| = e^{\alpha \log m} = m^{\alpha}. \tag{2.16}$$

We can also obtain an upper bound on α, for take $m = 2$. Since

$$| \, 2 \, | = | \, 1 + 1 \, | \leqslant 2,$$

we see that $2^\alpha \leqslant 2$, so $\alpha \leqslant 1$. Finally, let $| \; |_\infty$ denote the usual absolute value function. Then for $m > 1$, we have, using (2.16),

$$| \, m \, | = m^\alpha = | \, m \, |_\infty^\alpha \,, \qquad (2.17)$$

but $| -1 | = 1$ and $| -1 |_\infty = 1$, so (2.17) is true for all $m \in Z$, since it is also trivially true for $m = 0$. Applying Theorem 2.1, we have, for any $x \in Q$,

$$| \, x \, | = | \, x \, |_\infty^\alpha \,, \qquad \text{where} \qquad 0 < \alpha \leqslant 1.$$

We shall now show that all functions of the form $| \; |_\infty^\alpha$, where $0 < \alpha \leqslant 1$, and $| \; |_\infty$ still denotes the usual absolute value function, yield valuations of Q. Clearly conditions (2.1) and (2.2) are satisfied. To verify (2.3), we use Lemma 2.2; namely,

$$| \, x + y \, |_\infty^\alpha \leqslant (| \, x \, |_\infty + | \, y \, |_\infty)^\alpha \leqslant | \, x \, |_\infty^\alpha + | \, y \, |_\infty^\alpha \,.$$

Thus, we have completely solved the problem originally set forth. We have shown that any valuation of Q is either the trivial valuation, a p-adic valuation, or a power, $| \; |_\infty^\alpha$, of the ordinary absolute value, where $0 < \alpha \leqslant 1$.

We shall show that all valuations of the form $| \; |_\infty^\alpha$, $0 < \alpha \leqslant 1$, are equivalent in a sense which will presently be made precise. We also note that in defining the p-adic valuation $| \; |_p$ we chose a number c, $0 < c < 1$. If one chooses another real number d, $0 < d < 1$, instead of c, the resulting p-adic valuation will be equivalent to the original one, again, in a sense which we shall make precise. Before proceeding, however, to this notion of equivalent valuations, we wish to consider some further examples of valuations.

We shall now consider the field $k = F(x)$ of rational functions with coefficients from a field F. We wish to determine all valuations of k which are trivial on F. It follows immediately from Theorem 2.4 that any such valuation, $| \; |$, must be non-archimedian. As in the case with Q, there are two possibilities to consider. First, $|x| \leqslant 1$. Then, since $||$ is non-archimedian, and trivial on F, $|f(x)| \leqslant 1$ for all $f(x) \in F[x]$. If $|f(x)| = 1$ for all $f(x) \in F[x]$, other than 0, then, using Theorem 2.1, it is clear that $||$ is the trivial valuation. Thus, let us suppose that $|f(x)| < 1$ for some $f(x) \in F[x]$. We know, by Theorem 2.3, that the set of all such polynomials is a maximal ideal, and since $F[x]$ is a euclidean ring, this ideal must be a principal ideal generated by an irreducible polynomial $p(x)$. One also shows, as was done in the analogous case for Q, that $|f(x)| < 1$ if and only if $p(x) \mid f(x)$. Now, if $h(x) \in F(x)$, write

$$h(x) = p(x)^\alpha \, \frac{a(x)}{b(x)} \, ,$$

where $a(x)$, $b(x) \in F[x]$, and $p(x) \nmid a(x)$, $p(x) \nmid b(x)$. Then

$$| h(x) | = | p(x) |^\alpha = c^\alpha \qquad (2.18)$$

where $c = | p(x) |$, and $0 < c < 1$. One also shows, as in the case for Q, that all such functions of the form (2.18) yield valuations of $F(x)$.

For the second possibility, we consider $| x | > 1$. Let

$$f(x) = a_n x^n + a_{n-1} x^{n-1} + \cdots + a_1 x + a_0 \, .$$

Then $|f(x)| = | x |^n = | x |^{\deg f(x)} = c^{\deg f(x)}$, where $c = | x |$, and $c > 1$. Thus, if $h(x) \in F(x)$, $h(x) = f(x)/g(x)$, where $f(x)$, $g(x) \in F[x]$, and

$$| h(x) | = \frac{|f(x)|}{|g(x)|} = | x |^{\deg f - \deg g} = c^{\deg f - \deg g}; \qquad (2.19)$$

where $c > 1$. Again, it is easy to see that all functions of the form (2.19) yield valuations of $F(x)$.

As a natural extension of the p-adic valuations of Q and the case (2.18) for $F(x)$, we consider A to be any unique factorization domain. Then, if $x \in A$,

$$x = \epsilon \prod p^{\alpha_p} \, ,$$

where ϵ is a unit, and all but a finite number of the nonnegative integers $\alpha_p = 0$, and the p's are irreducible elements of A, which are not associate elements. We then define

$$| x |_p' = c^{\alpha_p}, \tag{2.20}$$

where $0 < c < 1$. The functions (2.20) satisfy conditions (2.1)–(2.3) on A, and are extended uniquely to the quotient field k by Theorem 2.1. All such functions are valuations of k, and (2.20) is called the p-adic valuation of k.

If $| \ |$ is a valuation of k, we can view k as a metric space with distance function, $d(x, y)$, $x, y \in k$, defined as

$$d(x, y) = | x - y |.$$

It follows immediately from the definition of valuation that this is, indeed, a legitimate distance function; that is,

$$d(x, y) \geqslant 0 \quad \text{and} \quad =0, \qquad \text{if and only if} \qquad x = y;$$

$$d(x, y) = d(y, x);$$

$$d(x, z) \leqslant d(x, y) + d(y, z).$$

If, in addition, $| \ |$ is non-archimedian, then d will satisfy the ultrametric inequality:

$$d(x, z) \leqslant \max (d(x, y), d(y, z)).$$

The proof is like the one in the first section for $| \ |_p$.

Once we have a metric space, we can introduce neighborhoods:

$$S(x, r) = \{y \in k \mid d(x, y) < r\}.$$

$S(x, r)$ is called the r neighborhood of x, or the spherical neighborhood of x with radius r. In terms of these neighborhoods, one can now introduce the usual topological notions of open set, closed set, compact set, convergence, etc.

3. Equivalent Valuations

Let $|\ |$ be a valuation on the field k. Also, let $\{a_n\}$ be a sequence of elements of k.

Definition 3.1. The sequence $\{a_n\}$ is called a *Cauchy sequence* with respect to the valuation $|\ |$ if, for any real number $\epsilon > 0$, there exists an integer N such that $|\ a_n - a_m\ | < \epsilon$ for all n, $m > N$.

In terms of the metric introduced at the end of Section 2, we could express this by writing $d(a_n,\ a_m) < \epsilon$ for all n, $m > N$.

Definition 3.2. The sequence $\{a_n\}$ is called a *null sequence* with respect to the valuation $|\ |$ if, for any real number $\epsilon > 0$, there exists an integer N such that $|\ a_n\ | < \epsilon$ for all $n > N$.

Again, in terms of the metric d, we could express this as $d(0, a_n) < \epsilon$ for $n > N$.

Now, let $|\ |_1$ and $|\ |_2$ be two nontrivial valuations of k.

Definition 3.3. The nontrivial valuations $|\ |_1$ and $|\ |_2$ are called *equivalent*, and we write $|\ |_1 \sim |\ |_2$, if $|\ a\ |_1 < 1$ implies $|\ a\ |_2 < 1$.

Clearly, if every null sequence with respect to $|\ |_1$ is a null sequence with respect to $|\ |_2$, then $|\ |_1 \sim |\ |_2$, for suppose $|\ a\ |_1 < 1$, then the sequence $\{a^n\}$ is a null sequence with respect to $|\ |_1$. Therefore, it is a null sequence with respect to $|\ |_2$, so we must have $|\ a\ |_2 < 1$.

We shall now investigate the relation $\sim$ between valuations. Clearly, $\sim$ is a reflexive and transitive relation. We shall presently see that it is also a symmetric relation, and, hence, is an equivalence relation. First, note that if $|\ |_1 \sim |\ |_2$, and if $|\ a\ |_1 > 1$, then $|\ a\ |_2 > 1$, for $|\ a\ |_1 > 1$ implies $|\ 1/a\ |_1 < 1$. Therefore, $|\ 1/a\ |_2 < 1$, or $|\ a\ |_2 > 1$.

Theorem 3.1. If $|\ |_1 \sim |\ |_2$, then $|\ a\ |_1 = 1$ implies that $|\ a\ |_2 = 1$.

Proof. Since $| \ |_1$ is not the trivial valuation, there exists an element $b \in k$, $b \neq 0$, such that $| \, b \, |_1 < 1$. Then

$$| \, a^n b \, |_1 = | \, a \, |_1{}^n \, | \, b \, |_1 < 1,$$

which implies that

$$| \, a^n b \, |_2 < 1, \quad \text{or} \quad | \, a \, |_2 < \Big(\frac{1}{| \, b \, |_2}\Big)^{1/n}.$$

If we let $n \to \infty$, then we get $| \, a \, |_2 \leqslant 1$. But if in place of a we use $1/a$, then we get $| \, 1/a \, |_2 \leqslant 1$, or $| \, a \, |_2 \geqslant 1$. Hence, $| \, a \, |_2 = 1$.

It now follows that $\sim$ is, indeed, a symmetric relation, for suppose $| \ |_1 \sim | \ |_2$, and suppose $| \, a \, |_2 < 1$. Then if $| \, a \, |_1 > 1$, we have $| \, a \, |_2 > 1$ by the comment just preceding this theorem. If $| \, a \, |_1 = 1$, then $| \, a \, |_2 = 1$ by the theorem. Thus, we must have $| \, a \, |_1 < 1$, i.e., $| \ |_2 \sim | \ |_1$.

We next wish to show that if $| \ |_1 \sim | \ |_2$, then $| \ |_2$ is just a power of $| \ |_1$. Once this statement has been established, then it is clear that if $| \ |_1 \sim | \ |_2$, any null sequence with respect to $| \ |_1$ is also a null sequence with respect to $| \ |_2$, which, together with the comment following Definition 3.3, would yield an alternate characterization of equivalent valuations.

Theorem 3.2. If $| \ |_1 \sim | \ |_2$, then $| \ |_2 = | \ |_1{}^\nu$, where ν is a positive real number.

Proof. We choose a fixed $b \in k$ such that $| \, b \, |_1 > 1$. Let $a \in k$, and $a \neq 0$. Then

$$| \, a \, |_1 = | \, b \, |_1{}^\alpha, \quad \text{where} \quad \alpha = \frac{\log | \, a \, |_1}{\log | \, b \, |_1}.$$

Now, let $n, m \in Z$ and $n/m > \alpha$. Then

$$| \, a \, |_1 < | \, b \, |_1{}^{n/m}, \quad \text{or} \quad \Big| \frac{a^m}{b^n} \Big|_1 < 1,$$

which implies, since $| \ |_1 \sim | \ |_2$, that

$$\Big| \frac{a^m}{b^n} \Big|_2 < 1.$$

Therefore,

$$| a |_2 < | b |_2^{n/m}.$$

In a similar fashion, one gets if $n/m < \alpha$, then

$$| a |_2 > | b |_2^{n/m}.$$

Hence, we must have

$$| a |_2 = | b |_2^{\alpha}.$$

Thus,

$$\alpha = \frac{\log | a |_1}{\log | b |_1} = \frac{\log | a |_2}{\log | b |_2},$$

so

$$\log | a |_2 = \frac{\log | b |_2}{\log | b |_1} \cdot \log | a |_1,$$

and if we let

$$\nu = \frac{\log | b |_2}{\log | b |_1},$$

then

$$| a |_2 = | a |_1^{\nu}.$$

Since the result is trivially true for $a = 0$, the proof of the theorem has been completed.

We next establish the important approximation theorem, which pertains to a finite number of inequivalent valuations. Before stating and proving this theorem, we establish two useful lemmas.

Lemma 3.1. Given n inequivalent (nontrivial, as usual) valuations $| \ |_i$, $i = 1, ..., n$ on a field k, there exists an element $a \in k$ such that $| a |_1 > 1$ and $| a |_i < 1$, $i = 2, ..., n$.

Proof. First, let $n = 2$. Then there exists an element $b \in k$ such that

$$| b |_1 > 1, \quad \text{and} \quad | b |_2 \leqslant 1$$

since $|\ |_1$ and $|\ |_2$ are not equivalent. Also, there exists an element $c \in k$ such that

$$|c|_1 \leqslant 1, \qquad \text{and} \qquad |c|_2 > 1$$

for the same reason. Now, let $a = b/c$. Then

$$|a|_1 = \frac{|b|_1}{|c|_1} > 1, \qquad \text{and} \qquad |a|_2 = \frac{|b|_2}{|c|_2} < 1.$$

We now assume that the lemma is true for $n - 1$ inequivalent valuations and proceed to the case of n inequivalent valuations. By the induction hypothesis, there exists an element $d \in k$ such that

$$|d|_1 > 1, \qquad \text{and} \qquad |d|_i < 1 \qquad \text{for} \qquad i = 2, ..., n - 1.$$

Also, there exists an element $c \in k$ such that

$$|c|_1 > 1, \qquad \text{and} \qquad |c|_n < 1$$

since $|\ |_1$ and $|\ |_n$ are inequivalent and since the lemma has been established for $n = 2$. Suppose first that $|d|_n \leqslant 1$. Then let $a = d^j c$ with j a sufficiently large positive integer:

$$|a|_1 = |d|_1^j |c|_1 > 1, \qquad |a|_n = |d|_n^j |c|_n < 1,$$

and, for $2 \leq i < n$,

$$|a|_i = |d|_i^j |c|_i < 1$$

if j is sufficiently large. Therefore, in this case, the element $a = d^j c$ for j sufficiently large works.

If, however, $|d|_n > 1$ let

$$a = \frac{d^j c}{1 + d^j}.$$

Then since

$$\left| \frac{d^j}{1 + d^j} - 1 \right|_1 = \left| \frac{1}{1 + d^j} \right|_1 = \left| \frac{(1/d)^j}{1 + (1/d)^j} \right|_1 \to 0,$$

we have that

$$\frac{d^j c}{1 + d^j} \to c.$$

It follows by (2.12) that $| a |_1$ is arbitrarily close to $| c |_1$ for j sufficiently large. Thus, $| a |_1 > 1$ for j sufficiently large. Now,

$$| a |_n \leqslant \frac{| d |_n{}^j | c |_n}{| d |_n{}^j - 1},$$

and, as above, the right-hand side of this inequality approaches $| c |_n$ as j gets large. Hence, $| a |_n < 1$ if j is sufficiently large. Finally, if $2 \leqslant i < n$, then

$$| a |_i \leqslant \frac{| d |_i{}^j | c |_i}{1 - | d |_i{}^j},$$

and the right-hand side of this inequality is arbitrarily small for j sufficiently large. Thus, in this case, $a = d^j c / 1 + d^j$ for j sufficiently large satisfies the conditions of the lemma.

Lemma 3.2. Let $| \ |_i$, $i = 1, ..., n$, be n (nontrivial) inequivalent valuations of a field k and let ϵ be an arbitrary positive real number. Then there exists an element $d \in k$ such that

$$| d - 1 |_1 < \epsilon, \qquad \text{and} \qquad | d |_i < \epsilon \qquad \text{for} \qquad i = 2, ..., n.$$

Proof. We choose an $a \in k$ which satisfies the conclusion of Lemma 3.1, and set

$$d = \frac{a^j}{1 + a^j}.$$

Then

$$| d - 1 |_1 = \left| \frac{-1}{1 + a^j} \right|_1 \leqslant \frac{1}{| a |_1{}^j - 1} < \epsilon$$

for j sufficiently large, where ϵ is any arbitrarily preassigned positive real number. Next, for $2 \leqslant i \leqslant n$,

$$| d |_i \leqslant \frac{| a |_i{}^j}{1 - | a |_i{}^j} < \epsilon$$

for j sufficiently large, and the proof of the lemma is completed.

Theorem 3.3 (the approximation theorem). Given n inequivalent (nontrivial) valuations $|\ |_i$, $i = 1, ..., n$, of k and n arbitrary elements a_i, $i = 1, ..., n$ of k, there exists an element $a \in k$ such that

$$| a - a_i |_i < \epsilon \qquad (i = 1, ..., n),$$

where ϵ is an arbitrarily given positive real number.

Proof. Lemma 3.2 guarantees that there exist elements $d_i \in k$ such that

$$| d_i - 1 |_i < \epsilon', \qquad \text{and} \qquad | d_i |_j < \epsilon' \qquad \text{for} \qquad j \neq i.$$

Let

$$a = a_1 d_1 + a_2 d_2 + \cdots + a_n d_n.$$

Then

$$\begin{aligned}
| a - a_i |_i &= | a_1 d_1 + \cdots + a_i(d_i - 1) + \cdots + a_n d_n |_i \\
&\leqslant | a_1 |_i\, \epsilon' + \cdots + | a_i |_i\, \epsilon' + \cdots + | a_n |_i\, \epsilon' \\
&< \epsilon,
\end{aligned}$$

for ϵ' sufficiently small, and the proof has been completed.

In the case of $k = Q$ and with $|\ |_i = |\ |_{p_i}$ as p_i-adic valuations, one can establish in a simpler fashion a much stronger version of the approximation theorem: not only does there exist an $a \in Q$ such that $| a - a_i |_{p_i} < \epsilon$ $(i = 1, ..., n)$, but $| a |_p \leqslant 1$ for all other p-adic valuations. We shall now establish this contention. First of all, we claim that it suffices to prove the statement where all elements involved are integers. Thus, given integers c_i, and distinct primes p_i $(i = 1, ..., m)$, and $\delta > 0$, suppose we can find an integer c such that

$$| c - c_i |_{p_i} < \delta \qquad (i = 1, ..., m), \qquad \text{and} \qquad | c |_p \leqslant 1$$

for all other primes p, then we show that the original problem has a solution; namely, let d be a common denominator of the a_i and take

$$c_i = d a_i \quad (i = 1, ..., n), \qquad \text{and} \qquad c_i = 0 \quad (i = n + 1, ..., m),$$

where $m - n$ equals the number of primes p for which $|d|_p \neq 1$, and, finally, let

$$\delta_1 = \min_{1 \leqslant i \leqslant n} |d|_{p_i} \epsilon, \qquad \delta_2 = \min_p |d|_p ,$$

where the minimum for δ_2 is taken over those p for which $|d|_p \neq 1$. Take

$$\delta = \min(\delta_1 , \delta_2).$$

Then there exists an integer c such that

$$|c - da_i|_{p_i} < \delta < |d|_{p_i} \epsilon \qquad (i = 1, ..., n)$$
$$|c - 0|_p < \delta < |d|_p$$

for those p such that $|d|_p \neq 1$, and

$$|c|_p \leqslant 1 = |d|_p$$

at all other primes. Thus, we have an integer c such that

$$|c - da_i|_{p_i} < |d|_{p_i} \epsilon \qquad (i = 1, ..., n),$$

and

$$|c|_p \leqslant |d|_p$$

at all other primes. Then, clearly, $a = c/d$ solves the original problem.

Now the condition $|a|_p \leqslant 1$ for an integer is automatically satisfied, so we must just see if we can satisfy the condition

$$|a - a_i|_{p_i} < \epsilon \qquad (i = 1, ..., n).$$

This means

$$a \equiv a_i \qquad (\mathrm{mod}\ p_i{}^{n_i}) \qquad (i = 1, ..., n),$$

with n_i sufficiently large. Since the moduli are relatively prime, one knows that these simultaneous congruences can be solved by the Chinese remainder theorem, (see Appendix) which completes the proof.

Exercises

1. Let the set X together with d be a metric space. Show that if d satisfies the ultrametric inequality, and if $d(x, y) \neq d(y, z)$, then

$$d(x, z) = \max\,(d(x, y), d(y, z)).$$

2. In the definition of the p-adic valuation, $|\ |_p$, take $c = 1/p$ (the *normalized* p-adic valuation). Show that if $x \in Q$ and $x \neq 0$, then

$$\prod_p |\,x\,|_p = \frac{1}{|\,x\,|_\infty},$$

where the product is taken over all primes p, and where $|\ |_\infty$ denotes the usual absolute value.

3. In a metric space X with distance function d, let $S_r(x)$ be the spherical neighborhood of x with radius r. Show that if d satisfies the ultrametric inequality, and if $z \in S_r(x)$, then $S_r(x) = S_r(z)$, i.e., every point inside a sphere is a center.

4. Let V be the valuation ring associated with the non-archimedian valuation $|\ |$. Let U be the set of all $a \in V$ such that $|\,a\,| = 1$. Show that U is a group (called the *group of units* of V).

5. Prove that any valuation of a field of characteristic not equal 0 is non-archimedian.

6. Prove that the only valuation of a finite field is the trivial valuation.

7. Show that the nontrivial valuations $|\ |_1$ and $|\ |_2$ are equivalent if and only if every Cauchy sequence with respect to $|\ |_1$ is a Cauchy sequence with respect to $|\ |_2$.

8. Assuming the stronger version of the approximation theorem in Q, prove the Chinese remainder theorem.

9. If $|\ |$ is a non-archimedian valuation of a field k, show that $\{x_n\}$ is a Cauchy sequence with respect to $|\ |$ if and only if $|\,x_{n+1} - x_n\,| \to 0$ as $n \to \infty$.

10. Let k be a field and $|\ |$ a valuation of k. Show that the field operations are continuous with respect to $|\ |$.

CHAPTER II

Complete Fields and the Field of p-Adic Numbers

1. Completion of a Field with Respect to a Valuation

As the reader is well aware from analysis and algebra, there are great advantages in passing from the field Q to the field R. One shortcoming of Q is the fact that not every Cauchy sequence of rational numbers converges to a rational number. These "gaps" in the field Q are filled in by a completion process which yields the field R. One way of achieving this completion is by Cantor's method, and it is this technique which will be applied to the more general situation which will confront us of an incomplete field with respect to a valuation. We must first, however, introduce some terminology.

We have already defined in I, 3 a Cauchy sequence $\{a_n\}$ of elements of a field k with respect to a valuation $|\ |$ in k.

Definition 1.1. Let k be a field and $|\ |$ a valuation on k. Let $\{a_n\}$ be a sequence of elements of k. The sequence $\{a_n\}$ is said to *converge* to the element $a \in k$ (and a is said to be a *limit* of $\{a_n\}$, denoted by $\lim a_n = a$, or $a_n \to a$) if, for every real number $\epsilon > 0$, there exists an integer N such that $|\ a_n - a\ | < \epsilon$ for all $n > N$.

In terms of the related metric of I, 2, this means $d(a_n, a) \to 0$ as $n \to \infty$.

The customary statements concerning limits which the reader is familiar with for real and complex numbers hold in our more general situation since the valuation satisfies the same conditions that the usual absolute value function does and which are needed in proving those statements.

Definition 1.2. The field k is called *complete* with respect to the valuation $|\ |$ if every Cauchy sequence of k with respect to $|\ |$ has a limit in k.

As noted, the field Q is not complete with respect to the usual absolute value, whereas, R and C are both complete with respect to the customary absolute values.

Before considering the general process of completing a field, we shall establish two useful results which hold in complete fields with respect to a valuation. If k is a complete field with respect to a valuation $|\ |$, we can introduce the notion of convergence of an infinite series $\sum_{n=1}^{\infty} a_n$, in the usual fashion. It follows immediately that if $\sum_{n=1}^{\infty} a_n$ converges, then $\lim a_n = 0$. It is useful to note that if $|\ |$ is non-archimedian, the converse statement holds, namely:

Theorem 1.1. If k is a complete field with respect to a non-archimedian valuation $|\ |$, and if $\{a_n\}$ is a sequence of elements of k such that $\lim a_n = 0$, then $\sum_{n=1}^{\infty} a_n$ converges.

Proof. Let

$$s_n = a_1 + \cdots + a_n, \qquad s_m = a_1 + \cdots + a_m,$$

where $m < n$. Then

$$|s_n - s_m| = |a_n + \cdots + a_{m+1}| \leqslant \max_{m+1 \leqslant i \leqslant n} |a_i| \to 0$$

as $n, m \to \infty$, which implies that $\lim s_n$ exists since k is complete. Therefore, $\sum_{n=1}^{\infty} a_n$ converges.

Theorem 1.2. If k is a complete field with respect to a valuation $|\ |$, and if $\{a_n\}$ is a sequence of elements of k such that $\sum_{n=1}^{\infty} |a_n|$ converges, then $\sum_{n=1}^{\infty} a_n$ converges.

Proof. Let $s_n' = |a_1| + \cdots + |a_n|$, $s_n = a_1 + \cdots + a_n$. Then, for $n > m$,

$$|s_n' - s_m'| = ||a_n| + \cdots + |a_{m+1}|| \tag{1.1}$$

where $|s_n' - s_m'|$ refers to the ordinary absolute value on R and similarly for the outer symbol $|\ |$ on the right of (1.1) embracing the sum. But

$$||a_n| + \cdots + |a_{m+1}|| = |a_n| + \cdots + |a_{m+1}|$$

since $|a_i| \geqslant 0$, and

$$|s_n - s_m| \leqslant |a_n| + \cdots + |a_{m+1}| \to 0$$

as $n, m \to \infty$ since $\sum_{n=1}^{\infty} |a_n|$ converges. Thus $|s_n - s_m| \to 0$ as $n, m \to \infty$, and, since k is complete, the theorem follows.

Now, we proceed to a discussion of the completion process. Given a field k with a valuation $|\ |$, we shall construct a complete field $\hat{k}$, called the completion of k, which contains a field $\tilde{k}$, isomorphic to k and such that $\tilde{k}$ is dense in $\hat{k}$. Moreover, $\hat{k}$ is unique up to an isomorphism. Actually a little more is true, not only is k isomorphic to $\tilde{k}$, but it is also *isometric* to $\tilde{k}$, i.e., the isomorphism preserves distances also. Also, $\hat{k}$ is unique up to an isometric isomorphism, or, more biefly, a *congruence*. We turn to the construction.

Let $\{a_n\}$ and $\{b_n\}$ be two Cauchy sequences of k with respect to $|\ |$. Introduce an addition and a multiplication between Cauchy sequences by defining:

$$\{a_n\} + \{b_n\} = \{a_n + b_n\}; \qquad \{a_n\}\{b_n\} = \{a_n b_n\}.$$

Let us show that the set of all Cauchy sequence is closed with respect to these operations. Clearly, $\{a_n + b_n\}$ is a Cauchy sequence since

$$|a_n + b_n - (a_m + b_m)| \leqslant |a_n - a_m| + |b_n - b_m|.$$

Since any Cauchy sequence is bounded, $\{a_n b_n\}$ is also a Cauchy sequence, for

$$
\begin{aligned}
|a_n b_n - a_m b_m| &= |a_n(b_n - b_m) + b_m(a_n - a_m)| \\
&\leqslant |a_n||b_n - b_m| + |b_m||a_n - a_m| \\
&\leqslant K_1|b_n - b_m| + K_2|a_n - a_m|,
\end{aligned}
$$

where $|a_n| \leqslant K_1$ for all n, and $|b_n| \leqslant K_2$ for all n. The contention is now clear. It is also clear that the set A of all Cauchy sequences of k with respect to these two operations is a ring with identity element.

Next, let $\{a_n\}$ and $\{b_n\}$ be null sequences. Since

$$| a_n - b_n | \leqslant | a_n | + | b_n |,$$

$\{a_n\} - \{b_n\}$ is a null sequence. If $\{c_n\}$ is a Cauchy sequence and if $\{a_n\}$ is a null sequence, then

$$| c_n a_n | \leqslant K | a_n |,$$

where $| c_n | \leqslant K$ for all n. Therefore, $\{c_n\} \{a_n\}$ is a null sequence, and it follows that the set M of all null sequences is an ideal in the ring A. We wish to show that M is actually a maximal ideal. First, observe that if the Cauchy sequence $\{a_n\}$ is not a null sequence, then there is an $\epsilon > 0$ and an integer N such that

$$| a_n | \geqslant \epsilon \qquad \text{for} \qquad n > N. \qquad (1.2)$$

For otherwise, for every $\epsilon > 0$ and every integer N, there exists an $n > N$ such that $| a_n | < \epsilon$. But there exists an integer N such that

$$| a_m - a_n | < \epsilon \qquad \text{for} \qquad n, m > N;$$

then

$$| a_m | \leqslant | a_n | + | a_m - a_n | < 2\epsilon$$

for every $\epsilon > 0$ provided $m > N$, which implies, contrary to our assumption, that $\{a_n\}$ is a null sequence, and, therefore, (1.2) has been established.

We continue to assume that $\{a_n\}$ is a Cauchy sequence which is not a null sequence so (1.2) holds. Define

$$b_n = \begin{cases} 0 & \text{for} \quad n \leqslant N \\ \dfrac{1}{a_n} & \text{for} \quad n > N. \end{cases} \qquad (1.3)$$

$\{b_n\}$ is a Cauchy sequence, for

$$| b_n - b_m | = \left| \frac{1}{a_n} - \frac{1}{a_m} \right|$$

$$= \left| \frac{a_m - a_n}{a_m a_n} \right|$$

$$\leqslant \frac{| a_m - a_n |}{\epsilon^2},$$

for $m, n > N$. The contention is now clear.

Next, we observe that

$$\{a_n\} \{b_n\} = \{0, 0, ..., 0, 1, 1, ...\}$$
$$= \{1, 1, ...\} - \{1, 1, ..., 1, 0, 0, ...\}.$$

Now let us show that M is, indeed, a maximal ideal. Suppose I is an ideal of A, and $I \supset M$ properly. Let $\{a_n\} \in I$ and $\{a_n\} \notin M$, i.e., $\{a_n\}$ is not a null sequence. Let $\{b_n\}$ be the corresponding Cauchy sequence constructed in (1.3). Then

$$\{b_n\} \{a_n\} \in I,$$

i.e.,

$$\{1, 1, ...\} - \{1, 1, ..., 1, 0, 0, ...\} \in I,$$

but $\{1, 1, ..., 1, 0, 0, ...\}$ is a null sequence, and is, therefore, also in I, so

$$\{1, 1, ...\} \in I,$$

which implies that $I = A$. Hence, M is maximal, and $\hat{k} = A/M$ is a field.

We introduce a valuation on $\hat{k}$, by defining for $\alpha = \{a_n\} + M \in \hat{k}$,

$$| \alpha | = \lim | a_n |. \tag{1.4}$$

We must show first of all that the limit in (1.4) exists, that it is well defined, and, finally, that is satisfies the axioms for a valuation. Since

$$|| a_n | - | a_m || \leqslant | a_n - a_m |,$$

$|a_n|$ is a Cauchy sequence of real numbers, and, therefore, has a limit. Next, if

$$\{a_n\} + M = \{b_n\} + M,$$

then

$$\{a_n - b_n\} = \{a_n\} - \{b_n\} \in M,$$

so

$$||a_n| - |b_n|| \leqslant |a_n - b_n| \to 0,$$

and $\lim |a_n| = \lim |b_n|$. Finally,

$$|\alpha| \geqslant 0, \quad \text{and} \quad =0 \qquad \text{if and only if} \qquad \lim |a_n| = 0,$$

i.e., if and only if $\{a_n\} \in M$, or $\alpha = M$.

If $\beta = \{b_n\} + M$. Then $\alpha\beta = \{a_n b_n\} + M$, and

$$|\alpha\beta| = \lim |a_n b_n| = \lim |a_n| \lim |b_n| = |\alpha| |\beta|.$$

$\alpha + \beta = \{a_n + b_n\} + M$, so

$$|\alpha + \beta| = \lim |a_n + b_n| \leqslant \lim |a_n| + \lim |b_n| = |\alpha| + |\beta|.$$

Now let $a \in k$. Consider the mapping:

$$f: \quad k \to A/M$$

given by

$$f(a) = \{a\} + M,$$

where $\{a\}$ designates here the Cauchy sequence $a, a, a, \ldots$. The claim is that f is an isomorphism of k onto

$$\tilde{k} = \{\{a\} + M \mid a \in k\}.$$

$$f(ab) = \{ab\} + M = (\{a\} + M)(\{b\} + M) = f(a)f(b).$$

$$f(a + b) = \{a + b\} + M = (\{a\} + M) + (\{b\} + M) = f(a) + f(b).$$

If $f(a) = 0$, then $\{a\} \in M$, i.e., $\{a\}$ is a null sequence; whence, $|a| = 0$, and $a = 0$. From (1.4),

$$|f(a)| = \lim |a| = |a|,$$

and f is, indeed, both an isomorphism and an isometry. We will identify k and $\tilde{k}$.

Next, we show that $\tilde{k}$ is dense in $\hat{k}$. Let $\alpha = \{a_n\} + M \in \hat{k}$, and let $\epsilon > 0$ be arbitrary. Then $|a_n - a_m| < \epsilon$ for $n, m > N$. We consider the element

$$\beta = \{a_n, a_n, a_n, \ldots\} + M \in \tilde{k},$$

where $n > N$:

$$|\beta - \alpha| = \lim_{m \to \infty} |a_n - a_m| \leqslant \epsilon,$$

so $\tilde{k}$ is dense in $\hat{k}$.

Now, we show that $\hat{k}$ is complete. First, let $a_1', a_2', \ldots, a_n', \ldots$ be a Cauchy sequence of $\tilde{k}$, where

$$a_n' = \{a_n, a_n, \ldots, a_n, \ldots\} + M.$$

Since $|a_n'| = |a_n|$,

$$a_1, a_2, \ldots, a_n, \ldots$$

is a Cauchy sequence, and

$$\lim a_n' = \alpha,$$

where $\alpha = \{a_n\} + M$ since

$$\lim_{n \to \infty} |\alpha - a_n'| = \lim_{n \to \infty} \lim_{m \to \infty} |a_m - a_n| = 0.$$

Now, let $\alpha_1, \alpha_2, \ldots, \alpha_n, \ldots$ be an arbitrary Cauchy sequence of $\hat{k}$. Since $\tilde{k}$ is dense in $\hat{k}$, we can find a sequence

$$a_1', a_2', \ldots, a_n', \ldots$$

of elements of $\tilde{k}$ such that

$$|a_n' - \alpha_n| < 1/n, \qquad n = 1, 2, \ldots.$$

Since

$$|a_m' - a_n'| \leqslant |a_m' - \alpha_m| + |\alpha_m - \alpha_n| + |\alpha_n - a_n'|$$

$a_1{}'$, $a_2{}'$, ..., $a_n{}'$, ... is a Cauchy sequence of elements of $\tilde{k}$, and, by what has just been shown, $\lim a_n{}' = \alpha$, where $\alpha \in \hat{k}$. But then α_1, α_2, ..., α_n, ... also converges to α since

$$| \alpha - \alpha_n | \leqslant | \alpha - a_n{}' | + | a_n{}' - \alpha_n |.$$

Thus, $\hat{k}$ is complete.

Suppose k_1 and k_2 are two complete fields with valuations $|\ |_1$ and $|\ |_2$ such that k is dense in k_1 and k_2, and such that $|\ |_1$ and $|\ |_2$ both extend the given valuation $|\ |$ on k, i.e., $| a |_1 = | a |_2 = | a |$ for $a \in k$. There exists a sequence

$$a_1, a_2, ..., a_n, ...$$

of elements of k such that $\lim a_n = \alpha_1$ where $\alpha_1 \in k_1$ since k is dense in k_1. $\{a_n\}$ is a convergent sequence, and is, therefore, certainly a Cauchy sequence. It can, moreover, be viewed as a Cauchy sequence of k_2 since $k_2 \supset k$ and $|\ |_2$ extends $|\ |$. Since k_2 is complete $\lim a_n = \alpha_2$, where $\alpha_2 \in k_2$. We now define a mapping,

$$f:\ k_1 \to k_2,$$

by $f(\alpha_1) = \alpha_2$. We contend that f is a congruence and that $f(a) = a$ for $a \in k$.

First, let us observe that the mapping is well defined. If

$$\lim a_n = \lim b_n = \alpha_1$$

in k_1, and $\lim a_n = \alpha_2$ in k_2, then

$$| \alpha_2 - b_n |_2 \leqslant | \alpha_2 - a_n |_2 + | a_n - b_n |,$$

and it follows that $\lim b_n = \alpha_2$ in k_2.

If $\lim a_n = \alpha_1$ and $\lim b_n = \beta_1$ in k_1, then $\lim (a_n + b_n) = \alpha_1 + \beta_1$ in k_1. While, if $\lim a_n = \alpha_2$ and $\lim b_n = \beta_2$, then $\lim (a_n + b_n) = \alpha_2 + \beta_2$ in k_2. From which we get

$$f(\alpha_1 + \beta_1) = f(\alpha_1) + f(\beta_1).$$

Similarly,

$$f(\alpha_1\beta_1) = f(\alpha_1)\,f(\beta_1),$$

so f is a homomorphism. f is clearly onto k_2 .

Furthermore, if

$$\lim a_n = \alpha_1, \qquad \text{and} \qquad \lim b_n = \beta_1 \quad \text{in} \quad k_1 ,$$

and

$$\lim a_n = \alpha_2, \qquad \text{and} \qquad \lim b_n = \beta_2 \quad \text{in} \quad k_2 ,$$

then, since

$$\mid \alpha_1 - \beta_1 \mid_1 \ \leqslant\ \mid \alpha_1 - a_n \mid_1 + \mid a_n - b_n \mid + \mid b_n - \beta_1 \mid_1 ,$$

we get

$$\mid \alpha_1 - \beta_1 \mid_1 \ \leqslant\ \lim \mid a_n - b_n \mid, \tag{1.5}$$

but

$$\mid a_n - b_n \mid \ \leqslant\ \mid a_n - \alpha_1 \mid_1 + \mid \alpha_1 - \beta_1 \mid_1 + \mid \beta_1 - b_n \mid_1 .$$

Hence,

$$\lim \mid a_n - b_n \mid \ \leqslant\ \mid \alpha_1 - \beta_1 \mid_1 . \tag{1.6}$$

Comparing (1.5) and (1.6), one sees that

$$\lim \mid a_n - b_n \mid \ =\ \mid \alpha_1 - \beta_1 \mid_1 . \tag{1.7}$$

A similar argument shows that

$$\lim \mid a_n - b_n \mid \ =\ \mid \alpha_2 - \beta_2 \mid_2 . \tag{1.8}$$

Thus,

$$\mid \alpha_1 - \beta \mid_1 \ =\ \mid \alpha_2 - \beta_2 \mid_2 ,$$

which shows that f is an isometry, and, therefore, certainly a one-one mapping, and we have shown that f is a congruence.

Finally, for $a \in k$, the sequence $\{a\}$ converges to a in both k_1 and k_2, so $f(a) = a$.

Summarizing and recalling our identification of k and $\tilde{k}$, we have:

Theorem 1.3. Given a field k and a valuation $| \: |$ on k, there exists a field $\hat{k}$ (unique up to a congruence), called the completion of k with respect to $| \: |$, such that $\hat{k}$ is a complete field with respect to a valuation extending $| \: |$, and k is dense in $\hat{k}$.

It is clear that $\hat{k}$ has the same characteristic as k, and if the given valuation is non-archimedian, then so is the extended valuation on $\hat{k}$.

Speaking somewhat loosely, we can summarize the completion process by saying that we associate with each Cauchy sequence which does not have a limit in k an "ideal" element and to equivalent Cauchy sequences we associate the same "ideal" element. These elements are then adjoined to k to yield the completion.

We shall denote by $| \: k \: |$ the image of k in R under the valuation mapping $| \: |$. We can now establish the following theorem.

Theorem 1.4. If $| \: |$ is a non-archimedian valuation on k, then $| \: k \: | = | \: \hat{k} \: |$, where $\hat{k}$ is the completion of k.

Proof. Let $\alpha \in \hat{k}$. If $\alpha = 0$, $| \: \alpha \: | = 0$. Suppose $\alpha \neq 0$. Since k is dense in $\hat{k}$, there exists a Cauchy sequence $\{a_n\}$ of elements of k such that $\lim a_n = \alpha$. However, $| \: |$ is non-archimedian, so

$$| \: a_n \: | = | \: \alpha + (a_n - \alpha) \: | = \max \left(| \: \alpha \: |, | \: a_n - \alpha \: | \right) = | \: \alpha \: |$$

for n sufficiently large by Theorem 2.2 of Chapter I since $| \: \alpha \: | \neq 0$ and $| \: a_n - \alpha \: |$ can be made arbitrarily small by taking n sufficiently large. Thus,

$$| \: a_n \: | = | \: \alpha \: |$$

for n sufficiently large, which establishes the theorem.

2. *p*-Adic Numbers

The completion of the field Q of rational numbers with respect to a *p*-adic valuation $| \: |_p$ is called the field of *p-adic numbers* and will be denoted Q_p. We shall also use $|\ |_p$ for the extension of $|\ |_p$ to Q_p.

Let $a \in Q_p$, and $\alpha \neq 0$. We know by Theorem 1.4 above that

$$|Q_p|_p = |Q|_p = \{|p|_p{}^n \mid n = 0, \pm1, \pm2, \pm3, ...\}$$

so

$$|\alpha|_p = |p|_p{}^n, \qquad (2.1)$$

and, therefore, $\alpha/p^n = \beta$ is a unit, i.e., $|\beta|_p = 1$. We shall denote by V, the valuation ring of $|\ |_p$ on Q, by P, the unique maximal ideal of V, by $\hat{V}$, the valuation ring of $|\ |_p$ on Q_p, and by $\hat{P}$, the unique maximal ideal of $\hat{V}$.

Clearly $\beta = \alpha/p^n \in \hat{V}$. But $\beta = \lim c_k$, where $c_k \in Q$. Thus $|\beta - c_k|_p < 1$ for k sufficiently large, say, for $k \geqslant N$. Hence,

$$|c_N|_p = |\beta + (c_N - \beta)|_p = \max(|\beta|_p, |c_N - \beta|_p) = |\beta|_p.$$

Therefore,

$$|c_N|_p = |\beta|_p = 1,$$

where $c_N \in Q$, and, therefore, $c_N \in V$. We now write $c_N = b_n$, so

$$|b_n|_p = 1, \quad \text{and} \quad |\beta - b_n|_p < 1, \quad \text{whence} \quad \beta + \hat{P} = b_n + \hat{P}.$$

Let $b_n = e_n/d_n$, where e_n, $d_n \in Z$, and where e_n and d_n are prime to p, which is possible since $|b_n|_p = 1$. Thus, there exist integers x and y such that

$$xd_n + yp = 1, \qquad \text{or} \qquad xd_n \equiv 1 \qquad (\mathrm{mod}\ p).$$

Then

$$\frac{e_n}{d_n} - e_n x = \frac{e_n(1 - d_n x)}{d_n} \equiv 0 \qquad (\mathrm{mod}\ P)$$

i.e., $b_n - e_n x \in P$, and, hence, $b_n - e_n x \in \hat{P}$.

If we let $e_n x = a_n$, then $a_n \in Z$, and

$$\beta + \hat{P} = b_n + \hat{P} = a_n + \hat{P}.$$

Now, $\mid a_n - \beta \mid_p < 1$, and we have

$$\mid a_n p^n - \beta p^n \mid_p < \mid p^n \mid_p, \qquad (2.2)$$

or

$$\alpha = \beta p^n = a_n p^n + (\beta - a_n) p^n$$
$$= a_n p^n + \gamma_1,$$

where $\gamma_1 = (\beta - a_n) p^n$, and $\mid \gamma_1 \mid_p < \mid p \mid_p^n$ by (2.2).

Thus $\mid \gamma_1 \mid_p = \mid p \mid_p^m$, where $m > n$, which is the same type of relation as we started with for α in (2.1). Hence, we treat γ_1 as we did α and continue the process. After k steps, we get

$$\alpha = a_n p^n + a_{n+1} p^{n+1} + \cdots + a_{n+k-1} p^{n+k-1} + \gamma_k,$$

where the $a_i \in Z$ and $\mid a_i \mid_p = 1$, or $a_i = 0$ and where

$$\mid \gamma_k \mid_p \leqslant \mid p \mid_p^{n+k}.$$

Since $\mid p \mid_p^{n+k} \to 0$ as $k \to \infty$, we have shown:

Theorem 2.1. Any p-adic number α can be written in the form

$$\alpha = \sum_n^\infty a_j p^j, \qquad (2.3)$$

where the $a_j \in Z$, and n is such that $\mid \alpha \mid_p = \mid p \mid_p^n$.

The integer coefficients of (2.3) are only unique modulo p. If we agree to choose the a_j such that $0 \leqslant a_j \leqslant p - 1$, then (2.3) will be called the *canonical* representation or expansion of α.

We illustrate by an example the canonical expansion. We shall determine the expansion of $\frac{3}{8}$ in Q_5, and shall adhere to the notation used in establishing Theorem 2.1. Since $\mid \frac{3}{8} \mid_5 = \mid 5 \mid_5^0 = 1$, we see that $n = 0$. A solution of

$$8x \equiv 1 \pmod 5$$

is $x = 2$, and, since $2 \cdot 3 \equiv 1 \pmod 5$, we get that $a_0 = 1$. Now

$$\gamma_1 = (\tfrac{3}{8} - 1) = -\tfrac{5}{8},$$

and $\left|-\frac{5}{8}\right|_5 = |\,5\,|_5^1$, which indicates that $a_1 \neq 0$, and $-(5/8 \cdot 5) = -\frac{1}{8}$. Again, a solution of

$$8x \equiv 1 \qquad (\text{mod } 5)$$

is $x = 2$, and $2(-1) \equiv 3 \,(\text{mod } 5)$. Thus $a_1 = 3$. Next,

$$\gamma_2 = (-\tfrac{1}{8} - 3)\, 5 = (-25/8)\, 5,$$

so $|\,\gamma_2\,|_5 = |\,5\,|_5^3$, which indicates that $a_2 = 0$, but $a_3 \neq 0$, and, since

$$\gamma_2/5^3 = -\tfrac{1}{8},$$

we see, as above, that $a_3 = 3$. Continuing, it is easy to see that

$$a_4 = a_6 = \cdots = 0, \qquad \text{while} \qquad a_5 = a_7 = \cdots = 3.$$

The expansion of $\alpha \in Q_p$, say

$$\alpha = \frac{a_{-\nu}}{p^\nu} + \frac{a_{-\nu+1}}{p^{\nu-1}} + \cdots + a_0 + a_1 p + a_2 p^2 + \cdots$$

is frequently abbreviated as follows:

$$\alpha = a_{-\nu} a_{-\nu+1} \cdots a_0 , \quad a_1 a_2 \cdots (p). \tag{2.4}$$

For example, we could write the canonical expansion of $\frac{3}{8}$ in Q_5 as

$$\tfrac{3}{8} = 1, 30\ 30\ 30 \cdots (5),$$

or, still shorter, as

$$\tfrac{3}{8} = 1, \overline{30} \cdots (5),$$

where the bar designates a periodic repetition.

If the element $\alpha \in Q_p$ has an expansion (2.3) for which $n \geqslant 0$, i.e., if

$$\alpha = a_0 , a_1 a_2 \cdots (p),$$

then α is called a *p-adic integer*. This will be the case if and only if $|\alpha|_p = |p|_p{}^n$ with $n \geqslant 0$, i.e., if and only if $\alpha \in \hat{V}$, the valuation ring of $|\ |_p$ on Q_p.

Let α be an arbitrary p-adic integer, $\alpha = \sum_0^\infty a_j p^j$. We let $s_n = \sum_0^{n-1} a_j p^j$. $\hat{V}p^n$ is the principal ideal generated by p^n in the ring V. Then

$$\alpha - s_n = p^n \left(\sum_{j=n}^\infty a_j p^{j-n} \right) = p^n \beta$$

where $\beta = \sum_{j=n}^\infty a_j p^{j-n} \in \hat{V}$, so

$$\alpha \equiv s_n \qquad (\mathrm{mod}\ \hat{V}p^n), \qquad n = 1, 2, \ldots \qquad (2.5)$$

where

$$s_{n+1} \equiv s_n \qquad (\mathrm{mod}\ \hat{V}p^n),$$

and each $s_n \in Z$. In other words, any p-adic integer satisfies an infinite system of congruences of the form (2.5).

Recalling our remarks immediately following Theorem 1.3 of the preceding section section and the subsequent representation (2.3) for any α of Q_p, we see that one could have initially defined the p-adic numbers as the totality of all formal series of the form $\sum_n^\infty a_j p^j$, where the $a_j \in Z$, and where two such series $\sum a_j p^j$, $\sum b_j p^j$ are considered equal if there exists an integer N such that

$$s_j = t_j + \beta p^j$$

for all $j \geqslant N$, where s_j and t_j are the sum of the first j terms of $\sum a_j p^j$ and $\sum b_j p^j$, respectively, and where $\beta \in Q$ and can be written as fraction with denominator prime to p. Then define the operations of addition and multiplication of two series in the natural fasion. The totality of all such series with respect to the two operations could then be shown to be a field.

Finally, we shall illustrate the arithmetic operations in Q_p using the notation introduced in (2.4). Before proceeding with specific examples, we note the following facts which will be useful for the examples. Since

$$a_i p^i + a_{i+1} p^{i+1} = (a_i + p) p^i + (a_{i+1} - 1) p^{i+1},$$

we have

$$a_{-\nu} a_{-\nu+1} \cdots a_0 , \cdots a_i a_{i+1} \cdots = a_{-\nu} a_{-\nu+1} \cdots a_0 , \cdots$$
$$a_i + p \, a_{i+1} - 1 \cdots . \quad (2.6)$$

Similarly,

$$a_{-\nu} \cdots a_0 , \cdots a_i a_{i+1} \cdots = a_{-\nu} \cdots a_0 , \cdots a_i - p \, a_{i+1} + 1 \cdots .$$
$$(2.7)$$

Equations (2.6) and (2.7) together with the next observation will enable us to write all elements obtained in our examples readily in the canonical expansion. We can write, say

$$a_{-\nu} = a'_{-\nu} + pt,$$

where $0 \leqslant a'_{-\nu} \leqslant p - 1$. Then

$$a_{-\nu} p^{-\nu} + a_{-\nu+1} p^{-\nu+1} = a'_{-\nu} p^{-\nu} + (t + a_{-\nu+1}) p^{-\nu+1}.$$

Next, we note that

$$0 = 00 \cdots p(p - 1) \cdots (p - 1), \quad (p - 1)(p - 1) \cdots .$$

Now, if $\alpha = \sum_n^\infty a_j p^j$ and $\beta = \sum_m^\infty b_j p^j$, then one obtains the expansion of $\alpha + \beta$ by adding "componentwise," and to get $\alpha\beta$, one multiplies the series formally and collects coefficients of the same powers of p, i.e., the usual Cauchy product, since one has convergence of the series with $| a_j p^j |_p$ in place of $a_j p^j$ and $| b_j p^j |_p$ in place of $b_j p^j$.

We consider now some specific examples and shall tacitly make use of the obervations made above.

(1) Addition. (a) In Q_7 add the following:

$$
\begin{array}{r}
452,1\,3\,7\,6\,1\,2 \\
+\ \ 37,5\,2\,1\,3\,1\,5\,2 \\
1\ \ 1\,1\ \ \ 1\,1\ \ \ \ 1 \\
\hline
413,0\,6\,1\,3\,3\,0\,3
\end{array}
$$

(b) In Q_5 add the following two elements and express the result in terms of the canonical expansion: $\frac{3}{8} + \frac{1}{5}$. We saw earlier that in Q_5

$$\tfrac{3}{8} = 1,303030 \cdots$$

while

$$\tfrac{1}{5} = 10,00000 \cdots .$$

Therefore,

$$\tfrac{3}{8} + \tfrac{1}{5} = 11,303030 \cdots .$$

(2) Multiplication. (a) Q_7 multiply the following:

$$
\begin{array}{r}
1\,2,3\,1\,4 \cdot 1,2\,0\,3 \\
\hline
1\,2\,3\,1\,4 \\
2\ 4\,6\,2\,8 \\
3\,6\,9\,3\,12 \\
1\ 1\,1\,2\ \ \ \ \ 1 \\
\hline
1\,4,0\,4\,6\,4\,5\,5\ \ \ 1
\end{array}
$$

(b) In Q_5 multiply $\frac{3}{8}$ and $\frac{1}{5}$ and express the result in canonical form. Clearly,

$$10,000 \cdots \cdot 1,3030 \cdots = 13,030303 \cdots .$$

(3) Subtraction. (a) In Q_7 subtract the following:

$$
\begin{array}{r}
5\,6,3\,5\,2\,4 \\
-\ \ 1,2\,4\,0\,3 \\
\hline
5\,5,1\,1\,2\,1
\end{array}
$$

(b) In Q_5 subtract the following:

$$
\begin{array}{r}
0\,5\,4,\,4\,4\,4\,4\,4\,4\, \cdots \\
2\,2\,1,\,4\,3\,0\,2\,1 \\
-\,1\,3\,4,\,2\,3\,1\,4\,2\,2 \\
\hline
1\,4\,1,\,6\,4\,3\,2\,3\,2\,4\,4\, \cdots \\
=\,1\,4\,1,\,1\,0\,4\,2\,3\,2\,4\,4\, \cdots
\end{array}
$$

(4) Division.   In Q_5 divide 32, 13 by 43, 12

$$
\begin{array}{r}
43,\,12 \mid 32,\,13 = 2,\,\overline{034430}\,\overline{034430} \\
32\ \ 34 \\
\hline
0\ \ 3444\, \cdots \\
3234 \\
\hline
11044\, \cdots \\
10241 \\
\hline
134244\, \cdots \\
10241 \\
\hline
323244\, \cdots \\
3234 \\
\hline
00344\, \cdots
\end{array}
$$

In the field R of real numbers one frequently writes a given number as a decimal expansion. The canonical expansion is the analog in Q_p. Also, in R an element is rational if and only if its decimal expansion is periodic. The analogous statement holds for Q_p.

Theorem 2.2.   An element $\alpha \in Q_p$ is rational if and only if its canonical expansion,

$$
\sum_{j=n}^{\infty} a_j p^j, \qquad 0 \leqslant a_j < p,
$$

where n is such that $|\,\alpha\,|_p = |\,p\,|_p{}^n$, is periodic.

Proof.   (1) Suppose the canonical expansion of α is periodic.

Then we can write α in the form

$$
\begin{aligned}
\alpha = &\; a_n p^n + a_{n+1} p^{n+1} + \cdots + a_{n+k} p^{n+k} \\
&+ b_1 p^{n+k+1} + b_2 p^{n+k+2} + \cdots + b_j p^{n+k+j} \\
&+ b_1 p^{n+k+j+1} + \cdots + b_j p^{n+k+2j} \\
&\cdots .
\end{aligned}
\tag{2.8}
$$

$$
\begin{aligned}
= &\; p^n(a_n + a_{n+1} p + \cdots + a_{n+k} p^k) \\
&+ p^{n+k+1}(b_1 + b_2 p + \cdots + b_j p^{j-1}) \\
&+ p^{n+k+j+1}(b_1 + b_2 p + \cdots + b_j p^{j-1}) \\
&+ \cdots .
\end{aligned}
$$

$$
= p^n A + p^{n+k+1} B (1 + p^j + p^{2j} + \cdots)
\tag{2.9}
$$

where

$$
A = a_n + a_{n+1} p + \cdots + a_{n+k} p^k,
$$

and

$$
B = b_1 + b_2 p + \cdots + b_j p^{j-1}.
$$

Then (2.9) equals

$$
p^n A + p^{n+k+1} B \, \frac{1}{1 - p^j}
\tag{2.10}
$$

since, in Q_p,

$$
1 + p^j + p^{2j} + \cdots + p^{(t-1)j} = \frac{1 - p^{tj}}{1 - p^j} \to \frac{1}{1 - p^j}
$$

as $t \to \infty$. However, (2.10) clearly is a rational number, which completes the first part of the proof.

(2) Assume, conversely, that $\alpha \in Q$. If we can write α in the form

$$
\alpha = \frac{p^n[A(p^j - 1) - B p^{k+1}]}{p^j - 1}
\tag{2.11}
$$

where $A, B \in Z$, and where $0 \leqslant A < p^{k+1}$, $0 \leqslant B < p^j$, then it follows that α has a periodic canonical expansion, for we can write (by the canonical expansion or see Appendix)

$$A = a_n + a_{n+1}p + \cdots + a_{n+k}p^k, \qquad 0 \leqslant a_i < p$$
$$B = b_1 + b_2 p + \cdots + b_j p^{j-1}, \qquad 0 \leqslant b_i < p,$$

and

$$\alpha = p^n A + p^{n+k+1} B \frac{1}{1 - p^j},$$

which implies that α can be written in the form (2.8) as we saw in the first part of the proof. Thus, we must just show that α can be written in the form (2.11). Let $\mid \alpha \mid_p = \mid p \mid_p{}^n$, so $\alpha/p^n = \beta$, where $\mid \beta \mid_p = 1$. Hence, we can write $\beta = c/d$, c, $d \in Z$, and $p \nmid d$, $p \nmid c$. Then there exists an integer j (see Appendix) such that

$$p^j \equiv 1 \qquad (\bmod\ d).$$

Now

$$\beta = \frac{c(p^j - 1)}{d(p^j - 1)},$$

and since $d \mid p^j - 1$, we have

$$\alpha = p^n \beta = p^n \frac{e}{p^j - 1}, \tag{2.12}$$

where $e \in Z$. Next, we choose an integer k such that

$$0 \leqslant e < p^{k+1} \text{ if } \alpha \geqslant 0; \quad -p^{k+1} \leqslant e < 0 \text{ if } \alpha < 0.$$

Since $(p^{k+1}, p^j - 1) = 1$, we can solve the congruence (see Appendix)

$$p^{k+1}x \equiv -e \qquad (\bmod\ p^j - 1)$$

uniquely modulo $p^j - 1$. Let B be a solution, where we take $0 \leqslant B \leqslant p^j - 2$ if $\alpha \geqslant 0$, and $1 \leqslant B \leqslant p^j - 1$ if $\alpha < 0$. Now,

$$p^{k+1}B \equiv -e \qquad (\bmod\ p^j - 1),$$

and, therefore,

$$e = A(p^j - 1) - Bp^{k+1}, \tag{2.13}$$

where $A \in Z$. It is easy to see that in both cases $0 \leqslant A < p^{k+1}$. Finally, substitution of (2.13) in (2.12) gives

$$\alpha = \frac{p^n[A(p^j - 1) - Bp^{k+1}]}{p^j - 1},$$

where $0 \leqslant A < p^{k+1}$, $0 \leqslant B < p^j$, which completes the proof.

3. Some Analysis in Q_p

In this section we shall consider the exponential, logarithmic, and binomial series in Q_p. Before doing so, we remind the reader of some facts already established (II, 1, Theorems 1.1 and 1.2) in a more general framework; namely, if $a_n \in Q_p (n = 0, 1, 2, ...)$ and $x \in Q_p$, then $\sum_{n=0}^{\infty} a_n x^n$ converges if and only if $\lim a_n x^n = 0$. Also, $\sum_{n=0}^{\infty} a_n x^n$ converges if $\sum_{n=0}^{\infty} |a_n x^n|_p$ converges. A series of the form $\sum_{n=0}^{\infty} a_n x^n$ is called a power series. The set of all x for which $\sum_{n=0}^{\infty} a_n x^n$ converges is called the *domain of convergence of the power series*, and, as in the case of the fields R or C with with the customary absolute values, one readily establishes that $\sum_{n=0}^{\infty} a_n x^n$ converges for $|x|_p < r$ and diverges for $|x|_p > r$, where

$$r = \frac{1}{\overline{\lim} \sqrt[n]{|a_n|_p}}.$$

The case $|x|_p = r$ is slightly easier to analyze here because of the non-archimedian character of the valuation; namely, for $|x|_p = r$, we have convergence if $\lim |a_n|_p r^n = 0$ and divergence if $\lim |a_n|_p r^n \neq 0$.

Other results follow readily as in the case of R or C. In many cases the proofs can be simplified slightly since $| |_p$ is a non-archimedian valuation. Thus, one has that if $\sum a_n x^n$ and $\sum b_n x^n$ converges, then $\sum (a_n \pm b_n) x^n$ converges and equals $\sum a_n x^n \pm \sum b_n x^n$. Similarly, the Cauchy product of $\sum a_n x^n$ and $\sum b_n x^n$ converges and equals $\sum a_n x^n \cdot \sum b_n x^n$.

If $f(x) = \sum_{n=0}^{\infty} a_n x^n$ converges, then $\lim a_n x^n = 0$, i.e., $\lim |a_n x^n|_p = 0$. Denoting $f'(x)$ as

$$f'(x) = \sum_{n=0}^{\infty} n a_n x^{n-1},$$

we have $|n a_n x^{n-1}|_p \leqslant |a_n x^{n-1}|_p \to 0$.

Therefore, $f'(x)$ converges. Moreover,

$$f'(x) = \lim_{y \to 0} \frac{f(x+y) - f(x)}{y}, \tag{3.1}$$

where $y \in Q_p$, and $y \neq 0$. Equation (3.1) follows readily from the following relations:

$$f(x+y) - f(x) = \sum_{n=0}^{\infty} a_n (x+y)^n - \sum_{n=0}^{\infty} a_n x^n$$

$$= \sum_{n=1}^{\infty} a_n \sum_{j=1}^{n} \binom{n}{j} x^{n-j} y^j,$$

so

$$\frac{f(x+y) - f(x)}{y} = \sum_{n=1}^{\infty} a_n \sum_{j=1}^{n} \binom{n}{j} x^{n-j} y^{j-1}. \tag{3.2}$$

But for $|y|_p < |x|_p$, we have

$$\left| a_n \binom{n}{j} x^{n-j} y^{j-1} \right|_p \leqslant |a_n|_p |x|_p^{n-1} \to 0,$$

i.e., the series in (3.2) converges uniformly for all y with $|y|_p < |x|_p$. Hence,

$$\lim_{y \to 0} \frac{f(x+y) - f(x)}{y} = \sum_{n=1}^{\infty} a_n \lim_{y \to 0} \sum_{j=1}^{n} \binom{n}{j} x^{n-j} y^{j-1}.$$

$$= \sum_{n=1}^{\infty} n a_n x^{n-1} = f'(x).$$

The other results follow just as simply as this one, and we shall make use of these results and similar ones in the sequel without further discussion.

It will be advantageous, for the discussion that follows to introduce some new notation. We know [see II, 1, Theorem 1.4 and also the beginning of Subsection 2] that if $x \in Q_p$, $x \neq 0$, then

$$| x |_p = | p |_p^n, \tag{3.3}$$

where $n = 0, \pm1, \pm2, \dots$. We denote by $\mathrm{ord}_p x$, called the *ordinal* of x at p, the integer n occurring in (3.3). Thus,

$$| x |_p = | p |_p^{\mathrm{ord}_p x}, \tag{3.4}$$

or $| x |_p = c^{\mathrm{ord}_p x}$, where $c = | p |_p$, and $0 < c < 1$. For $x = 0$, we define $\mathrm{ord}_p x = \infty$. It is clear that

$$
\begin{aligned}
| x |_p = 1 &\Leftrightarrow \mathrm{ord}_p x = 0. \\
| x |_p < 1 &\Leftrightarrow \mathrm{ord}_p x > 0. \\
| x |_p > 1 &\Leftrightarrow \mathrm{ord}_p x < 0.
\end{aligned}
\tag{3.5}
$$

We also have that

$$\mathrm{ord}_p xy = \mathrm{ord}_p x + \mathrm{ord}_p y, \tag{3.6}$$

which follows immediately from $| xy |_p = | x |_p | y |_p$. Also, from $| x + y |_p \leqslant \max(| x |_p, | y |_p)$, one gets

$$\mathrm{ord}_p (x + y) \geqslant \min(\mathrm{ord}_p x, \mathrm{ord}_p y). \tag{3.7}$$

We know [I, (2.12)] that if $x_n \in Q_p$ and $x_n \to x$, then $| x_n |_p \to | x |_p$. In terms of ordinals, this means that if

$$x_n \to x, \quad \text{then} \quad \mathrm{ord}_p x_n \to \mathrm{ord}_p x. \tag{3.8}$$

As a final consideration before discussing the exponential function, we establish the following useful lemma.

Lemma 3.1.   Let n be a positive integer, and let

$$n = a_0 + a_1 p + \cdots + a_t p^t, \qquad 0 \leqslant a_i \leqslant p - 1$$

be the canonical representation of n. Then

$$\operatorname{ord}_p (n!) = \frac{n - s_n}{p - 1},$$

where $s_n = a_0 + a_1 + \cdots + a_t$.

Proof.   For notational convenience, we shall write $s_0 = 0$. Let $1 \leqslant k \leqslant n$, and suppose

$$k = 0, 0\,0\,0 \cdots 0 \quad b_\nu b_{\nu+1} \cdots b_t,$$

is the canonical expansion of k where $b_\nu \geqslant 1$, i.e.,

$$k = b_\nu p^\nu + b_{\nu+1} p^{\nu+1} + \cdots + b_t p^t, \qquad s_k = b_\nu + b_{\nu+1} + \cdots + b_t.$$

Then

$$\begin{aligned}
k - 1 = {} & (p - 1) + (p - 1)\, p + \cdots + (p - 1)\, p^{\nu-1} \\
& + (b_\nu - 1)\, p^\nu + b_{\nu+1} p^{\nu+1} + \cdots + b_t p^t
\end{aligned}$$

and

$$\begin{aligned}
s_{k-1} &= \nu(p - 1) + (b_\nu - 1) + b_{\nu+1} + \cdots + b_t \\
&= \nu(p - 1) + s_k - 1.
\end{aligned}$$

Hence,

$$\nu = \frac{s_{k-1} - s_k + 1}{p - 1},$$

but clearly $\nu = \operatorname{ord}_p k$. Therefore,

$$\operatorname{ord}_p k = \frac{s_{k-1} - s_k + 1}{p - 1}$$

and, by (3.6), we have

$$\operatorname{ord}_p (n!) = \frac{1}{p - 1} \sum_{k=1}^{n} (s_{k-1} - s_k + 1) = \frac{n - s_n}{p - 1},$$

which establishes the lemma.

We shall now consider the exponential series $E(x) = \sum_{n=0}^{\infty} x^n / n!$.

First of all, we wish to determine the domain of convergence of this series. The answer is given in the following theorem.

Theorem 3.1. The domain of convergence of the exponential series, $E(x) = \sum_{n=0}^{\infty} x^n/n!$, is the set of all x for which $\operatorname{ord}_p x > 1/(p - 1)$.

    Proof. By (3.6) and the lemma, we have

$$\operatorname{ord}_p \left(\frac{x^n}{n!} \right) = n \operatorname{ord}_p x - \operatorname{ord}_p (n!)$$

$$= n \operatorname{ord}_p x - \left(\frac{n - s_n}{p - 1} \right)$$

$$= n \left(\operatorname{ord}_p x - \frac{1}{p - 1} \right) + \frac{s_n}{p - 1}.$$

Thus, if $\operatorname{ord}_p x > 1/(p - 1)$, then $\operatorname{ord}_p (x^n/n!) \to \infty$, i.e., $|x^n/n!|_p \to 0$, and the series converges. If, however, $\operatorname{ord}_p x \leqslant 1/(p - 1)$, then for all n of the form p^k, $s_n = 1$, and, for such n, $\operatorname{ord}_p (x^n/n!) \not\to \infty$. Thus, the series converges for those and only those x with $\operatorname{ord}_p x > 1/(p - 1)$.

    In particular, if $x \in Z$ and if p is an odd prime, then for $x = kp$, $k \in Z$, $\operatorname{ord}_p x \geqslant 1 > 1/(p - 1)$, and the exponential series converges for such an x. If however, $p = 2$ and if $x \in Z$, then x must be a multiple of 4 in order for x to belong to the domain of convergence of the exponential series.

    It follows immediately from the unconditional convergence of our series that if x and y belong to the domain of convergence of the exponential series, then

$$E(x + y) = E(x) E(y). \tag{3.9}$$

We also note some other relevant facts concerning the exponential series, which will play a role subsequently. If

$$\operatorname{ord}_p x > \frac{1}{p - 1}, \qquad x \neq 0,$$

then $$\tag{3.10}$$

$$\operatorname{ord}_p \left(\frac{x^n}{n!} \right) > \operatorname{ord}_p x \qquad \text{for} \qquad n > 1.$$

The result (3.10) follows immediately from the following relations:

$$\text{ord}_p\left(\frac{x^n}{n!}\right) - \text{ord}_p x = n\,\text{ord}_p x - \text{ord}_p n! - \text{ord}_p x$$

$$= (n-1)\,\text{ord}_p x - \frac{n}{p-1} + \frac{s_n}{p-1}$$

$$> \frac{n-1}{p-1} - \frac{n}{p-1} + \frac{s_n}{p-1} = \frac{s_n-1}{p-1} \geqslant 0.$$

Finally, we note if x belongs to the domain of convergence of the exponential series, then

$$\text{ord}_p\,(E(x) - 1) = \text{ord}_p x. \tag{3.11}$$

Equation (3.11) follows from the following considerations:

$$E(x) - 1 = x + \frac{x^2}{2!} + \cdots + \frac{x^n}{n!} + \cdots,$$

or

$$E(x) - 1 = \lim s_n(x),$$

where $s_n(x) = x + x^2/2! + \cdots + x^n/n!$. Recalling Theorem 2.2 of Chapter I and (3.10) above, we have

$$\text{ord}_p\,s_n(x) = \text{ord}_p\left(x + \frac{x^2}{2!} + \cdots + \frac{x^n}{n!}\right) = \text{ord}_p x.$$

Now,

$$\text{ord}_p\,(E(x) - 1) = \text{ord}_p \lim s_n(x)$$
$$= \lim \text{ord}_p\,s_n(x) \qquad [\text{by (3.8)}]$$
$$= \lim \text{ord}_p x = \text{ord}_p x,$$

and (3.11) has been proved.

We turn now to a consideration of the logarithmic series.

Theorem 3.2. The domain of convergence of the logarithmic series, $\log(1 + x) = \sum_{n=1}^{\infty} (-1)^{n-1} x^n / n$, is the set of all x for which $\operatorname{ord}_p x > 0$.

Proof. We have

$$\operatorname{ord}_p \left(\frac{(-1)^{n-1} x^n}{n} \right) = n \operatorname{ord}_p x - \operatorname{ord}_p n. \qquad (3.12)$$

However, it is clear that

$$p^{\operatorname{ord}_p n} \leqslant n,$$

and, therefore,

$$\operatorname{ord}_p n \leqslant \frac{\log n}{\log p}.$$

Inserting this last estimate in (3.12) shows that if $\operatorname{ord}_p x > 0$, then

$$\operatorname{ord}_p \left(\frac{(-1)^{n-1} x^n}{n} \right) \to \infty,$$

and the series converges. If $\operatorname{ord}_p x \leqslant 0$, then for those n such that $p \nmid n$, $\operatorname{ord}_p n = 0$, and

$$\operatorname{ord}_p \left(\frac{(-1)^{n-1} x^n}{n} \right) \nrightarrow \infty.$$

Hence, the domain of convergence consists precisely of those x for which $\operatorname{ord}_p x > 0$.

It follows readily that the logarithm function satisfies the functional equation

$$\log(1 + x)(1 + y) = \log(1 + x) + \log(1 + y), \qquad (3.13)$$

where $\operatorname{ord}_p x > 0$, and $\operatorname{ord}_p y > 0$. We also note the following facts which are analogous to (3.10) and (3.11): if

$$\operatorname{ord}_p x > \frac{1}{p - 1}, \qquad x \neq 0, \qquad (3.14)$$

then

$$\text{ord}_p \left(\frac{(-1)^{n-1}x^n}{n} \right) > \text{ord}_p x \qquad \text{for} \qquad n > 1,$$

and

$$\text{ord}_p \left(\log (1 + x) \right) = \text{ord}_p x. \tag{3.15}$$

Once (3.14) has been established, (3.15) follows form it in the same fashion as (3.11) followed from (3.10). Thus, we just prove (3.14). Let $\text{ord}_p x > 1/(p - 1)$, and $x \neq 0$. Then

$$\text{ord}_p \left(\frac{(-1)^{n-1}x^n}{n} \right) - \text{ord}_p x = n \, \text{ord}_p x - \text{ord}_p n - \text{ord}_p x$$

$$= (n - 1) \, \text{ord}_p x - \text{ord}_p n$$

$$> \frac{n - 1}{p - 1} - \text{ord}_p n$$

$$= (n - 1) \left(\frac{1}{p - 1} - \frac{\text{ord}_p n}{n - 1} \right). \tag{3.16}$$

Now, let us suppose that $n = p^\alpha a$, where $p \nmid a$, so $\text{ord}_p n = \alpha$. Then

$$\frac{\text{ord}_p n}{n - 1} = \frac{\alpha}{p^\alpha a - 1} \leqslant \frac{\alpha}{p^\alpha - 1}$$

$$= \frac{1}{p - 1} \cdot \frac{\alpha}{p^{\alpha-1} + \cdots + p + 1} \leqslant \frac{1}{p - 1},$$

and it follows from this and (3.16) that

$$\text{ord}_p \left(\frac{(-1)^{n-1}x^n}{n} \right) - \text{ord}_p x > 0.$$

We are now in a position to show the interrelation between the exponential and logarithmic functions, namely:

Theorem 3.3. If $\operatorname{ord}_p x > 1/(p-1)$, then (1) $\log E(x) = x$, and (2) $E(\log (1 + x)) = 1 + x$.

Proof. (1) is clear for $x = 0$. We next observe that $\log E(x)$ converges since, by (3.11),

$$\operatorname{ord}_p (E(x) - 1) = \operatorname{ord}_p x > \frac{1}{p-1} > 0.$$

Finally, since $E'(x) = E(x)$, we have

$$(\log E(x))' = \frac{E'(x)}{E(x)} = 1,$$

so $\log E(x) = a + x$, where a is a constant in Q_p, and for $x = 0$, we get $a = 0$; whence,

$$\log E(x) = x.$$

Statement (2) is also clear for $x = 0$. Next, $E(\log (1 + x))$ converges since, by (3.15)

$$\operatorname{ord}_p (\log (1 + x)) = \operatorname{ord}_p x > \frac{1}{p-1}.$$

Now, by the first part of the theorem, we have

$$\log E(\log (1 + x)) = \log (1 + x),$$

which implies (see Exercise 7 at the end of this chapter) that

$$E(\log (1 + x)) = 1 + x.$$

We conclude this section with a brief discussion of the binomial series.

Theorem 3.4. Let $y \in Q_p$ be such that $\operatorname{ord}_p y \geqslant 0$ (i.e., $y \in \hat{V}$, the valuation ring of $|\;|_p$ on Q_p). The binomial series, $(1 + x)^y = \sum_{n=0}^{\infty} \binom{y}{n} x^n$, converges for all x with $\operatorname{ord}_p x > 1/(p-1)$.

Proof. Since $\operatorname{ord}_p y \geqslant 0$, and since

$$\binom{y}{n} = \frac{y(y - 1) \cdots (y - (n - 1))}{n!},$$

it is easily seen that

$$\operatorname{ord}_p \binom{y}{n} \geqslant \operatorname{ord}_p \left(\frac{1}{n!}\right).$$

Thus,

$$\operatorname{ord}_p \left(\binom{y}{n} x^n\right) \geqslant \operatorname{ord}_p \frac{(x^n)}{n!},$$

but, as we saw in the proof of Theorem 3.1, $\operatorname{ord}_p (x^n/n!) \to \infty$ if $\operatorname{ord}_p x > 1/(p-1)$, and this completes the proof of the theorem.

From the proof of Theorem 3.4, we have for all y with $\operatorname{ord}_p y \geqslant 0$

$$\left|\binom{y}{n} x^n\right|_p \leqslant \left|\frac{x^n}{n!}\right|_p \to 0$$

for $\operatorname{ord}_p x > 1/(p-1)$. Thus the series converges uniformly in y, and since each $\binom{y}{n}$ is clearly a continuous function of y, it follows that $(1+x)^y$ is a continuous function of y.

Finally, one can show for $y \in Q_p$, $\operatorname{ord}_p y \geqslant 0$, and $\operatorname{ord}_p x > 1/(p-1)$,

$$(1+x)^y = E(y \log (1+x)), \text{ and } \log (1+x)^y = y \log (1+x).$$

We leave these final considerations to the reader to justify.

4. Newton's Method in Complete Fields

Let k be a complete field with respect to a non-archimedian valuation $|\ |$; also, let V be the associated valuation ring. We might think, in view of the applications that will be presented later, of k as a p-adic field and of $|\ |$ as $|\ |_p$. We want to show that if certain polynomial equations have an approximate root in k, then they have a root in k, i.e., we shall extend Newton's method to this case. More precisely, we prove:

Theorem 4.1. Let $f(x)$ be a polynomial with coefficients in V, the valuation ring associated with $|\ |$ in the complete field k.

Suppose also that $f(x)$ has leading coefficient 1. If there exists an $\alpha_1 \in k$ such that

$$|f(\alpha_1)| < 1 \qquad \text{and} \qquad |f'(\alpha_1)| = 1,$$

then the sequence

$$\alpha_2 = \alpha_1 - \frac{f(\alpha_1)}{f'(\alpha_1)}$$

$$\alpha_3 = \alpha_2 - \frac{f(\alpha_2)}{f'(\alpha_2)} \tag{4.1}$$

$$\cdots\cdots\cdots\cdots\cdots$$

converges to a root $\alpha \in V$ of $f(x)$.

Proof.   Observe first of all that $\alpha_1 \in V$, for if

$$f(x) = x^n + a_{n-1}x^{n-1} + \cdots + a_0 ,$$

where the $a_i \in V$, then

$$f(\alpha_1) = \alpha_1^n + a_{n-1}\alpha_1^{n-1} + \cdots + a_0 . \tag{4.2}$$

If $|\alpha_1| > 1$, then the first term of (4.2) would be the dominant term with respect to the valuation, and we would have $|f(\alpha_1)| > 1$, a contradiction.

Now, by Taylor's theorem,

$$f(x + h) = f(x) + hf'(x) + h^2g(x, h),$$

namely, $f(x) = \sum_{i=0}^n a_ix^i$, where $a_i \in V$, and $a_n = 1$.
Then

$$f(x + h) = \sum_{i=0}^n a_i(x + h)^i$$

$$= f(x) + hf'(x) + h^2f_2(x) + h^3f_3(x) + \cdots + h^nf_n(x)$$

$$= f(x) + hf'(x) + h^2g(x, h),$$

where $g(x, h) = f_2(x) + hf_3(x) + \cdots + h^{n-2}f_n(x)$.

Thus,

$$f(\alpha_2) = f\left(\alpha_1 - \frac{f(\alpha_1)}{f'(\alpha_1)}\right)$$

$$\qquad\qquad (4.3)$$

$$= f(\alpha_1) - \frac{f(\alpha_1)}{f'(\alpha_1)} f'(\alpha_1) + \left(\frac{f(\alpha_1)}{f'(\alpha_1)}\right)^2 g\left(\alpha_1, -\frac{f(\alpha_1)}{f'(\alpha_1)}\right),$$

but

$$g\left(\alpha_1, -\frac{f(\alpha_1)}{f'(\alpha_1)}\right) = f_2(\alpha_1) + \left(\frac{-f(\alpha_1)}{f'(\alpha_1)}\right)f_3(\alpha_1) + \cdots.$$

Now, the coefficients of the f_i are all in V, and $\alpha_1 \in V$, and $|f(\alpha_1)/f'(\alpha_1)| < 1$, so

$$\left| g\left(\alpha_1, -\frac{f(\alpha_1)}{f'(\alpha_1)}\right)\right| \leqslant 1.$$

Hence, from (4.3) and the hypothesis, we obtain

$$|f(\alpha_2)| \leqslant |f(\alpha_1)|^2.$$

Again, by Taylor's theorem

$$f'(x + h) = f'(x) + hF(x, h),$$

so

$$f'(\alpha_2) = f'(\alpha_1) - \frac{f(\alpha_1)}{f'(\alpha_1)} F\left(\alpha_1, \frac{-f(\alpha_1)}{f'(\alpha_1)}\right),$$

but

$$\left|\frac{f(\alpha_1)}{f'(\alpha_1)}\right| < 1, \quad \text{and} \quad \left| F\left(\alpha_1, \frac{-f(\alpha_1)}{f'(\alpha_1)}\right)\right| \leqslant 1.$$

Therefore,

$$|f'(\alpha_2)| = |f'(\alpha_1)| = 1.$$

Hence, α_2 satisfies the same two assumptions as α_1, and we may proceed with the iteration. Thus,

$$| \alpha_2 - \alpha_1 | = | f(\alpha_1) |$$
$$| \alpha_3 - \alpha_2 | = | f(\alpha_2) | \leqslant | f(\alpha_1) |^2$$
$$| \alpha_4 - \alpha_3 | \leqslant | f(\alpha_1) |^4$$
$$\cdots\cdots\cdots\cdots\cdots\cdots\cdots\cdots\cdots\cdots\cdots\cdots$$
$$| \alpha_n - \alpha_{n-1} | \leqslant | f(\alpha_1) |^{2^{n-2}}$$
$$\cdots\cdots\cdots\cdots\cdots\cdots\cdots\cdots\cdots\cdots\cdots\cdots$$

Finally, set

$$\alpha = \alpha_1 + (\alpha_2 - \alpha_1) + (\alpha_3 - \alpha_2) + \cdots$$
$$= \lim \alpha_n .$$

The series converges since its nth term approaches 0. Also, since

$$| f(\alpha_n) | \leqslant | f(\alpha_1) |^{2^{n-1}},$$

it is clear that $f(\alpha) = 0$. We also note that $| \alpha - \alpha_1 | = \lim | \alpha_n - \alpha_1 |$, but

$$| \alpha_n - \alpha_1 | \leqslant \max_{2 \leqslant i \leqslant n} | \alpha_i - \alpha_{i-1} | < 1,$$

so $| \alpha - \alpha_1 | \leqslant 1$, and $\alpha \in V$. The proof is now complete.

We wish to modify the hypothesis of the preceding theorem just slightly in view of a subsequent application, namely:

Theorem 4.2. Let $f(x)$ be a polynomial with coefficients in V, the valuation ring associated with the valuation $|\ |$ in the complete field k, and suppose the leading coefficient of $f(x)$ is 1. If there exists an $\alpha_1 \in k$ such that

$$| f(\alpha_1) | < 1, \qquad f'(\alpha_1) \neq 0, \qquad | f'(\alpha_1) | \leqslant 1,$$

and for

$$d_1 = \frac{f(\alpha_1)}{f'(\alpha_1)^2}, \qquad | d_1 | < 1,$$

then the sequence (4.1) converges to a root $\alpha \in V$ of $f(x)$.

Proof. As in the proof of Theorem 4.1, $\alpha_1 \in V$. Clearly,

$$|\alpha_2 - \alpha_1| = |d_1| |f'(\alpha_1)|.$$

Again, by Taylor's theorem,

$$f(\alpha_2) = f\left(\alpha_1 - \frac{f(\alpha_1)}{f'(\alpha_1)}\right)$$

$$= f(\alpha_1) - \frac{f(\alpha_1)}{f'(\alpha_1)} \cdot f'(\alpha_1) + \left(\frac{f(\alpha_1)}{f'(\alpha_1)}\right)^2 \cdot \beta, \qquad (4.4)$$

where $\beta \in V$ since

$$-\frac{f(\alpha_1)}{f'(\alpha_1)} = -d_1 f'(\alpha_1) \in V.$$

Thus,

$$|f(\alpha_2)| \leqslant |f(\alpha_1)| |d_1|. \qquad (4.5)$$

Also,

$$f'(\alpha_2) = f'\left(\alpha_1 - \frac{f(\alpha_1)}{f'(\alpha_1)}\right) = f'(\alpha_1) - \frac{f(\alpha_1)}{f'(\alpha_1)} \cdot \gamma,$$

where $\gamma \in V$, so

$$f'(\alpha_2) = f'(\alpha_1)(1 + d_1\gamma),$$

and

$$|f'(\alpha_2)| = |f'(\alpha_1)| |1 + d_1\gamma| = |f'(\alpha_1)|.$$

Hence,

$$f'(\alpha_2) = f'(\alpha_1) \epsilon, \qquad (4.6)$$

where ϵ is a unit, i.e., $|\epsilon| = 1$. Now, by (4.4) and (4.6),

$$d_2 = \frac{f(\alpha_2)}{f'(\alpha_2)^2} = \frac{(f(\alpha_1)^2/f'(\alpha_1)^2) \cdot \beta}{f'(\alpha_1)^2 \cdot \epsilon^2} = \frac{f(\alpha_1)^2}{f'(\alpha_1)^4} \cdot \delta$$

where $\delta \in V$. Therefore,

$$|d_2| \leqslant |d_1|^2.$$

Proceeding inductively, we get

$$|\alpha_{n+1} - \alpha_n| = |d_n| |f'(\alpha_n)|$$
$$= |d_n| |f'(\alpha_1)|$$
$$\leqslant |d_1|^{2^{n-1}} |f'(\alpha_1)|.$$

Then, as before, we set

$$\alpha = \alpha_1 + (\alpha_2 - \alpha_1) + (\alpha_3 - \alpha_2) + \cdots$$
$$= \lim \alpha_n,$$

and conclude that the series converges, $f(\alpha) = 0$, and $\alpha \in V$.

We now want to consider several applications of the previous theorems to the case of the p-adic fields. First, take $k = Q_5$ and $f(x) = x^2 + 1$. Let $\alpha_1 = 2$. Then

$$f(2) = 5, \quad \text{so} \quad |f(2)|_5 < 1, \quad f'(2) = 4, \quad \text{so} \quad |f'(2)|_5 = 1.$$

Thus, by Theorem 4.1, the sequence (4.1) converges to a root α of $f(x)$:

$$\alpha^2 + 1 = 0, \quad \text{i.e.,} \quad \sqrt{-1} \in Q_5.$$

We note that it suffices for the applications of either theorem to the case of Q_p to try and find an $\alpha_1 \in Z$, for, by the remarks at the beginning of Section 2, since $\alpha_1 \in \hat{V}$, the valuation ring of $| \ |_p$ on Q_p,

$$\alpha_1 + \hat{P} = a + \hat{P},$$

where $a \in Z$, and where $\hat{P}$ is the unique maximal ideal of $\hat{V}$.

We also note that for the above example, we could apply Theorem 3.4 of the preceding section, namely,

$$\sqrt{-1} = \tfrac{1}{2}\sqrt{1 - 5}.$$

$y = \tfrac{1}{2} \in Q_5$ and $\text{ord}_5 \tfrac{1}{2} = 0$; while, $\text{ord}_5 (-5) = 1 > 1/(5 - 1)$. Thus

$$\sqrt{-1} = \frac{1}{2}\sum_{n=0}^{\infty} (-1)^n \binom{\tfrac{1}{2}}{n} 5^n.$$

As our next application, we want to consider, in general, when the equation $f(x) = x^2 - a$ can be solved in Q_p, where $a \in Z$, and $p^2 \nmid a$. Suppose, first, that $p \mid a$. If $x^2 - a$ has a solution $\sqrt{a} \in Q_p$, then

$$\sqrt{\mid a \mid_p} = \mid \sqrt{a} \mid_p, \qquad (4.7)$$

since

$$\mid a \mid_p = \mid \sqrt{a}\,\sqrt{a} \mid_p = \mid \sqrt{a} \mid_p \mid \sqrt{a} \mid_p.$$

Now, from (4.7) and our assumption,

$$\mid \sqrt{a} \mid_p = \mid p \mid_p^{1/2}. \qquad (4.8)$$

However, as we know (see beginning of Section 2)

$$\mid Q_p \mid_p = \{\mid p \mid_p^n \mid n = 0, \pm 1, \pm 2, \cdots\},$$

which contradicts (4.8). Thus, if $p \mid a$, $\sqrt{a} \notin Q_p$.

Let us now assume that $p \nmid a$. To apply Theorem 4.1, we must see if there exists an $\alpha_1 \in Z$ such that

$$\mid f(\alpha_1) \mid_p = \mid \alpha_1{}^2 - a \mid_p < 1, \quad \text{and} \quad \mid f'(\alpha_1) \mid_p = \mid 2\alpha_1 \mid_p = 1.$$

The first condition means that

$$\alpha_1{}^2 \equiv a \pmod{p},$$

i.e., a is a quadratic residue modulo p. The second condition means that $p \nmid 2\alpha_1$. Suppose $p \neq 2$, and $\alpha_1{}^2 \equiv a \pmod{p}$. Then

$$p \mid \alpha_1{}^2 - a,$$

but $p \nmid a$. Therefore, $p \nmid \alpha_1$ and, since $p \neq 2$, $p \nmid 2\alpha_1$. Thus, in this case, if a is a quadratic residue modulo p, then $x^2 - a$ has two solutions in Q_p.

If a is a quadratic nonresidue modulo p, then it is easy to see that $x^2 - a$ has no solution in Q_p, for if $\alpha \in Q_p$ and if

$$\alpha^2 - a = 0,$$

then $\alpha \in \hat{V}$, and

$$\alpha + \hat{P} = b + \hat{P},$$

where $b \in Z$. We then have

$$a + \hat{P} = \alpha^2 + \hat{P} = b^2 + \hat{P},$$

which implies that

$$b^2 \equiv a \qquad (\text{mod } p).$$

However, this contradicts the fact that a is a quadratic non-residue modulo p. Summarizing, we have:

Theorem 4.3. If p is an odd prime, then the equation $x^2 - a = 0$, where $a \in Z$, and $p^2 \nmid a$ has:

(1) no solution in Q_p if $p \mid a$;

(2) two or no solutions in Q_p according as a is a quadratic residue modulo p or a quadratic nonresidue modulo p if $p \nmid a$.

Finally, let us consider the case $p = 2$, where $2 \nmid a$. Here we shall apply Theorem 4.2, for it is clear that one cannot find an α_1 satisfying the criteria of Theorem 4.1. We, therefore, seek an $\alpha_1 \in Z$ such that

$$|f(\alpha_1)|_2 = |\alpha_1{}^2 - a|_2 < 1, \qquad \text{and} \qquad |d_1|_2 < 1,$$

where

$$d_1 = \frac{f(\alpha_1)}{f'(\alpha_1)^2} = \frac{\alpha_1{}^2 - a}{4\alpha_1{}^2}.$$

Since $2 \nmid \alpha_1{}^2$, we see that it suffices to have $8 \mid \alpha_1{}^2 - a$ so that both conditions will be satisfied. Thus, we must be able to solve the congruence

$$x^2 \equiv a \qquad (\text{mod } 8)$$

with an α_1 such that

$$\alpha_1 \equiv 1 \qquad (\text{mod } 2),$$

i.e., α_1 should be odd. But for any odd integer, α_1,

$$\alpha_1{}^2 \equiv 1 \qquad (\text{mod } 8).$$

Hence, we see that if $a \equiv 1 \pmod 8$, then we can use any odd integer α_1, and the criteria of Theorem 4.2 will be satisfied.

Conversely, if α is a solution of $x^2 - a = 0$ in Q_2, then $\alpha \in \hat{V}$, and by II, (2.5),

$$\alpha \equiv b \pmod{\hat{V}2^3}$$

where $b \in Z$. Thus,

$$a = \alpha^2 \equiv b^2 \pmod{\hat{V}2^3},$$

and it follows immediately from this and from the fact that b must be odd that

$$a \equiv b^2 \equiv 1 \pmod 8.$$

Summarizing, in this case, we have:

Theorem 4.4. The equation $x^2 - a = 0$, where $a \in Z$, $4 \nmid a$ has in Q_2

(1) no solution if $2 \mid a$;

(2) two or no solutions according as a is or is not congruent 1 modulo 8 if $2 \nmid a$.

It is clear that the field Q_p is topologically distinct from the field Q_q for $p \neq q$ since in Q_p the sequence p, p^2, ..., p^n, ... converges to 0, while this is certainly not the case in Q_q (see also Exercise 12 at the end of this chapter). With the aid of Theorems 4.3 and 4.4, one can also show that they are algebraically distinct, namely:

Theorem 4.5. If p and q are distinct primes, then the fields Q_p and Q_q are not ismorphic.

Proof. We consider first the case where p and q are odd primes and, say, $p > q$. If there were an isomorphism between Q_p and Q_q, then the additive and multiplicative identities of the two fields would correspond, and, consequently, so would the elements of the rational subfields. If p is a quadratic residue modulo q, then, by Theorem 4.3, the equation $x^2 - p = 0$ has a solution in Q_q but no solution in Q_p. However, this contradicts the assumption that the fields are isomorphic, for if $\alpha^2 = p$ in Q_q, then the image of α under the isomorphism would be a solution of the equation in Q_p. Now consider the case where p is a quadratic nonresidue modulo q. Select a quadratic nonresidue, n, modulo q such that $n < q$; n certainly exists since q is odd. Then np is a quadratic residue modulo q. Hence, again by Theorem 4.3, the equation

$$x^2 - np = 0$$

has a solution in Q_q, but no solution in Q_p since $n < q < p$, so $p^2 \nmid np$. Thus, the theorem has been established if p and q are distinct odd primes.

Now let p be any odd prime. If 2 is a quadratic residue modulo p, then, using both Theorems 4.3 and 4.4, we see that the equation

$$x^2 - 2 = 0$$

has a solution in Q_p but no solution in Q_2. If 2 is a quadratic nonresidue modulo p, select an odd quadratic nonresidue, n, modulo p, which certainly exists, for if m is an even quadratic nonresidue modulo p, $m + p$ is an odd one. Now, $2n$ is a quadratic residue modulo p. Therefore, the equation

$$x^2 - 2n = 0$$

has a solution in Q_p. However, it has no solution in Q_2 since $4 \nmid 2n$, but $2/2n$.

Since all cases have been considered, the proof of the theorem has been completed.

5. Roots of Unity in Q_p

We shall show that the equation

$$x^{p-1} - 1 = 0 \tag{5.1}$$

has exactly $p - 1$ distinct roots in Q_p. Since Q_p is a field, Eq. (5.1) has at most $p - 1$ roots in Q_p. Let a represent any of the integers $1, 2, ..., p - 1$. Consider

$$\alpha = a + (a^p - a) + (a^{p^2} - a^p) + \cdots \qquad (5.2)$$
$$= \lim a^{p^n}.$$

The series is readily seen to converge since the nth term,

$$a^{p^{n+1}} - a^{p^n} = a^{p^n}(a^{p^n(p-1)} - 1),$$

and

$$a^{p^n(p-1)} \equiv 1 \qquad (\bmod \ p^{n+1}) \qquad (5.3)$$

by Euler's theorem (see Appendix). Thus, the nth term approaches zero, and the series converges. Also,

$$\alpha^{p-1} = \lim a^{p^n(p-1)} = 1$$

by (5.3). Hence, α is a solution of (5.1), i.e., a $(p - 1)$ root of unity. Letting a assume the different values $1, 2, ..., p - 1$, (5.2) is seen to yield $p - 1$ distinct roots of (5.1). Clearly each root α of (5.1) belongs to $\hat{V}$, the valuation ring of $|\ |_p$ on Q_p. Also, different roots belong to distinct residue classes modulo $\hat{P}$, the unique maximal ideal of $\hat{V}$, for if α and β are roots of (5.1), say,

$$\alpha = a + (a^p - a) + (a^{p^2} - a^p) + \cdots,$$
$$\beta = b + (b^p - b) + (b^{p^2} - b^p) + \cdots,$$

where $a \neq b$, and $1 \leqslant a, b \leqslant p - 1$, then

$$\alpha + \hat{P} = \beta + \hat{P}$$

implies that

$$a + \hat{P} = b + \hat{P},$$

or

$$a \equiv b \qquad (\bmod \ p),$$

which is impossible.

Recalling the discussion preceding Theorem 2.1 of this

chapter, we see now that another canonical type representation is possible, i.e., any $\gamma \in Q_p$ can be written uniquely in the form

$$\gamma = \sum_{n}^{\infty} a_j p^j,$$

where the α_j are either 0 or are $(p - 1)$ roots of unity.

Exercises

1. Find the canonical representation of the following elements:

    (a) $\frac{1}{5}$ in Q_3.   (b) $\frac{1}{3}$ in Q_2.   (c) $\frac{-5}{7}$ in Q_5.

2. Perform the indicated operations in Q_5.

  (a)   123, 412 (b)   124, 131 (c) $(34, 121) \cdot (0, 2103)$.
      $+$ 421, 032 $-$ 321, 221 (d) $(131, 2) \div (2, 42)$.

3. In Q_3, what rational number has the canonical expansion

$$2, \overline{0121}\ 0121 \cdots ?$$

4. In books on number theory (see e.g. Bibliography) it is shown that

$$\operatorname{ord}_p n! = \left[\frac{n}{p}\right] + \left[\frac{n}{p^2}\right] + \left[\frac{n}{p^3}\right] + \cdots,$$

where $[x]$ denotes the largest integer $\leqslant x$. Use this result to give an alternate proof that

$$\operatorname{ord}_p n! = \frac{n - s_n}{p - 1}.$$

5. Suppose x and y belong to the domain of convergence of the exponential series. Show if $E(x) = E(y)$, then $x = y$.

6. Show that it is not necessarily true that

$$\operatorname{ord}_p \left(\frac{(-1)^{n-1} x^n}{n}\right) - \operatorname{ord}_p x > 0 \quad \text{if} \quad \operatorname{ord}_p x \leqslant \frac{1}{p - 1}.$$

7. Show if $\text{ord}_p\, x > \dfrac{1}{p-1}$ and $\text{ord}_p\, y > \dfrac{1}{p-1}$, and if $\log(1+x) = \log(1+y)$, then $x = y$.

8. In Q_3 determine the first few terms of the canonical expansion of $\log 4$.

9. Prove that the equation $x^2 + x + a = 0$, where $a \in Z$, has a solution in Q_2 if and only if a is even.

10. Use the result of Exercise 9 to give an alternate proof that Q_2 is not isomorphic to Q_p for $p \neq 2$.

11. Let $\hat{k}$ be the completion of k with respect to a non-archimedian valuation $|\,|$. If V is the valuation ring associated with $|\,|$ on k, let $\bar{V}$ be the closure of V in $\hat{k}$. Show that $\bar{V} = \hat{V}$, the valuation ring of the extended valuation on $\hat{k}$. Similarly, show that $\bar{P} = \hat{P}$, where P is the unique maximal ideal of V, and $\hat{P}$, the unique maximal ideal of $\hat{V}$.

12. Show that the sequence $q, q^2, \ldots, q^n, \ldots$ has a converging subsequence in Q_p; where q is a prime not equal to p. Does the sequence itself converge in Q_p?

13. Consider the sequence of primes

$$2, 3, 5, 7, 11, \ldots \quad \text{in} \quad Q_p\,.$$

Find a convergent subsequence.

14. Using the notation of Exercise 11, and taking $k = Q$ and $11 = 11_p$, show that for any $\epsilon > 0$, there exists a finite set of elements $a_1, \ldots, a_n$ depending on ϵ in $\hat{V}$ such that for any $\alpha \in \hat{V}$, there exists an a_i with $|\alpha - a_i| < \epsilon$.

15. Using the notation of Exercise 14, show that $\hat{V}$ is compact.

CHAPTER III

Valuation Rings, Places, and Valuations

1. Valuation Rings and Places

In this chapter, we want to extend some of the notions already introduced in Chapter I. In particular, we want to extend the notion of non-archimedian valuations of rank one, which we had been dealing with throughout most of the first two chapters. We shall first consider valuation rings in general—a special case of which was already considered in Chapter I. Then we shall see the intimate connection between this concept and those of places and valuations. Next, we shall consider a general extension theorem for places. This theorem will be basic in discussing the possibilities of extending a non-archimedian valuation on a given field to a finite extension field, which we shall come to in Chapter V. Finally, we shall give an application of our results to the concept of integral closure.

Throughout this section, K will denote an arbitrary field.

Definition 1.1. A subring V of K is called a *valuation ring* if $a \in K$ and if $a \notin V$, then $a^{-1} \in V$.

It is clear that if K is a field and $| \ |$ is a rank one valuation on K, then the valuation ring associated with the valuation in I, Theorem 2.3 is a valuation ring in the sense of Definition 1.1. It is also clear that an arbitrary field K is itself a valuation ring, which we shall call the *trivial valuation ring*.

It follows immediately from the definition that if V is a valuation ring, $1 \in V$, where 1 is the identity element of the multiplicative group of the field K.

We consider now the set P of non-units of the valuation ring V, i.e.,

$$P = \{a \in V \mid a^{-1} \notin V\} \tag{1.1}$$

Lemma 1.1. If P is defined as in (1.1), then $a \notin P \Leftrightarrow a^{-1} \in V$.

Proof. Suppose $a \notin P$. If $a \in V$, then, by the definition of P, $a^{-1} \in V$. If $a \notin V$, then, by definition of V, $a^{-1} \in V$.

Conversely, suppose $a^{-1} \in V$. If $a \in V$, then $a \notin P$ by definition of P. If $a \notin V$, then clearly $a \notin P$. This completes the proof of the lemma.

The set P considered in Theorem 2.3 of Chapter I certainly satisfies condition (1.1). There we saw that P is the unique maximal ideal of V. We can prove the corresponding statement here for the set P of (1.1) with the aid of the lemma. First note:

(1)   If $a + b \notin P$, then either $a \notin P$ or $b \notin P$.

Proof. The statement is clear if either $a = 0$ or $b = 0$. Hence, we may assume that both a and b are not 0. We may also assume, and do, that $a/b \in V$, for if $a/b \notin V$, then $b/a \in V$, since V is a valuation ring, and the argument would be analogous. Now, since $a + b \notin P$, by Lemma 1.1

$$(a + b)^{-1} \in V.$$

Therefore,

$$b^{-1} = \left(1 + \frac{a}{b}\right)(a + b)^{-1} \in V,$$

and, again by Lemma 1.1, $b \notin P$.

We may reword (1) as follows:

(1′)   If a and b belong to P, then $a + b \in P$.

Next, we have

(2)   If $a, b \in V$ and if $ab \notin P$, then $a \notin P$ and $b \notin P$.

Proof. Since $ab \notin P$, Lemma 1.1 implies that $(ab)^{-1} \in V$. Therefore,

$$a^{-1} = (ab)^{-1}\, b \in V,$$

so $a \notin P$. Similarly $b \notin P$.

We may also reword (2) as follows:

(2′)   If $a, b \in V$ and if either a or b belongs to P, then $ab \in P$.

Statements (1′) and (2′) imply that P is an ideal of V. If I is an ideal of V and if I is not contained in P, then I contains a unit of V; whence, $I = V$. Thus, P is the unique maximal ideal of V. Since P is maximal and since $1 \in V$, V/P is a field, called the *residue class field*, and P is a prime ideal.

Again, we denote by V a valuation ring of K, and we let U denote the units of V, i.e.,

$$U = \{a \in V \mid a^{-1} \in V\}.$$

It is clear that U is a multiplicative group, which will be called the *group of units* of V.

We now claim that the field K decomposes into the following disjoint union:

$$K = P \cup U \cup (P - \{0\})^{-1}, \qquad (1.2)$$

where $P - \{0\}$ denotes the difference set, and $(P - \{0\})^{-1}$ denotes the set of elements inverse to those of $P - \{0\}$. Since $P \cup U = V$, in order to prove (1.2), all one must show is that $K - V = (P - \{0\})^{-1}$. Thus, suppose that $a \in K - V$, so $a \notin V$, and, therefore, $a^{-1} \in V$, and $a^{-1} \in P$, so $a \in (P - \{0\})^{-1}$. Conversely, if $a \in (P - \{0\})^{-1}$, then $a^{-1} \in P$. Hence, $a \notin V$, and, therefore, $a \in K - V$.

It is easy to see from (1.2) that if V_1 and V_2 are two valuation rings of K with non-units P_1 and P_2 and units U_1 and U_2, respectively, then

$$V_1 \subset V_2 \Leftrightarrow P_1 \supset P_2 \Leftrightarrow U_1 \subset U_2.$$

The next concept that we want to introduce is that of a place. Although a place is intimately related with a non-archimedian valuation, we did not point this out in the introductory chapters, but now we shall proceed to consider the relationship. Actually, in a sense, the reader is acquainted with places, as we shall point out in some of the illustrative examples which will follow the definitions.

Definition 1.2. Let K and F be arbitrary fields. A map $\phi : K \to F \cup \{\infty\}$ is called a *place* if:

(1) $\phi^{-1}(F) = V$ is a ring;

(2) the restriction of ϕ to V, $\phi\,|_V$, is a nontrivial homo-
morphism;

(3) if $\phi(a) = \infty$, then $\phi(a^{-1}) = 0$.

We shall give some examples of places.

(a) Let $K = F(x)$, the field of rational functions of a transcendental element x over F with coefficients in the field F. Write
each element of $F(x)$ in reduced form. If we substitue $x = a \in F$
in each element, we obtain a well-defined mapping

$$K = F(x) \to F \cup \{\infty\}$$

under the specification that if, after the substitution, 0 appears in
the denominator then that element is mapped into ∞. It is a
simple matter to verify that this mapping is, indeed, a place.
Thus, one might view a place intuitively as a substitution mapping.

(b) Let $K = Q$, and let p be a fixed prime. Take $F = Z/(p)$,
where (p) is the principal ideal generated by p in Z. Now, write
any $\beta \in Q$ in the form $\beta = a/b$, where not both a and b are
divisible by p. Consider the following map

$$Q \to Z/(p) \cup \{\infty\}$$

defined as follows: replace a and b by the residue classes to which
they belong modulo p, and, should the denominator be the 0
residue class, map the element into ∞. Again, it is readily seen that
we have a place. Actually, the first example follows the same
procedure as this one, for, if $f(x) \in F[x]$, then, by the division
algorithm

$$f(x) = (x - a)\, q(x) + f(a), \quad \text{and} \quad f(x) \equiv f(a) \bmod (x - a),$$

i.e., in this example, we considered residue classes modulo
$(x - a)$ in the ring $F[x]$.

Now, we wish to draw some consequences from the definition
of a place. The first observation is that if ϕ is a place, where
$\phi : K \to F \cup \{\infty\}$, then

$V = \phi^{-1}(F)$ is valuation ring, called the valuation
ring *associated* with the given place. The proof is

immediate, for if $a \notin V$, then $\phi(a) = \infty$, and, (1.3)
therefore, $\phi(a^{-1}) = 0$; hence, $a^{-1} \in V$, and V is a
valuation ring.

Let us consider the non-units, P, of this valuation ring. By
(1.2), we know that P consists of the 0 element and the inverses
of those elements which do not belong to V. Thus, by definition
of the place ϕ,

$$\phi(P) = 0. \tag{1.4}$$

Suppose $a \in V$, and $\phi(a) = 0$. If $a^{-1} \in V$, then

$$\phi(1) = \phi(aa^{-1}) = \phi(a)\,\phi(a^{-1}) = 0,$$

which implies that $\phi(V) = 0$, but this contradicts the fact that
ϕ is nontrivial. This together with (1.4) shows that the kernel of ϕ
on V is precisely P.

We have seen, up to this point, that, with a given place, there
is an associated valuation ring, V. Now we shall show that the
converse is true, namely, given a valuation ring of a field K a
place can be associated with it. Denote by P the maximal ideal of
non-units of V, and define

$$\phi(a) = \begin{cases} \infty & \text{if} \quad a \notin V \\ a + P & \text{if} \quad a \in V \end{cases} \tag{1.5}$$

Thus, on V, ϕ is defined to be the canonical homomorphism onto
the quotient ring V/P, which is a field F. Clearly, ϕ satisfies
condition (1) of Definition 1.2, and, on V, ϕ is a nontrivial
homomorphism since $1 \notin P$, so condition (2) is satisfied. Finally
if $a \notin V$, then $a \in (P - \{0\})^{-1}$, so $a^{-1} \in P$. Hence, condition (3) is
satisfied. The valuation ring associated with the place ϕ is the
given valuation ring V.

The place ϕ so constructed will be called the place *associated*
with the given valuation ring.

We return now to the situation where a place $\phi: K \to F \cup \{\infty\}$ is
given and denote by V, the associated valuation ring, so

$$\phi\,|_V: \quad V \to F$$

is a homomorphism with kernel P, as has been noted. Hence, the map $\phi \mid V$ decomposes into the product of 3 maps: $\phi \mid_V = i f \kappa'$, where

$$V \xrightarrow{\kappa} V/P \xrightarrow{f} \phi \mid_V (V) \xrightarrow{i} F,$$

and κ is the canonical homomorphism, f is an isomorphism, and i is the injection map. If we extend κ to $K - V$ by taking $\kappa(a) = \infty$ for all $a \in K - V$, then this would be the place (1.5) associated with the valuation ring V. We can, therefore, state the following: There exists a one-to-one correspondence between places and valuation rings, where by this we mean the following: a given place determines an associated valuation ring, which, in turn, determines an associated place, which is equal to the given place up to an isomorphism.

Two places are called *equivalent* if they have the same associated valuation ring. Thus, we can reword the above result by saying that there is a one-to-one correspondence between places and valuation rings up to an equivalency.

2. Valuations

We shall, in this section, consider a more general notion of valuations than we did in Chapter I, and we shall then interrelate this concept to those of places and valuation rings. Before doing this, however, we must define what is meant by an ordered group.

Definition 2.1. Let G be a multiplicative group. The group G is said to be an *ordered group* if G contains a normal subsemigroup S such that

$$G = S \cup \{1\} \cup S^{-1}, \tag{2.1}$$

where the union is a disjoint one, and where S^{-1} denotes the set of all inverses of elements of S.

Now, let G be an ordered group and define

$$a < b \quad \text{if and only if} \quad ab^{-1} \in S, \quad \text{where } a, b \in G. \tag{2.2}$$

In particular, $a < 1$ if and only if $a \in S$. We shall show that

$<$ satisfies the customary order relationships. We note first that $a < b$ will also be denoted at times by $b > a$.

(1) $a < b$ if and only if $b^{-1}a \in S$.

Proof. $b^{-1}a = b^{-1}(ab^{-1})\,b$.

Therefore, if $ab^{-1} \in S$, then $b^{-1}a \in S$ since S is normal. Similarly, since

$$ab^{-1} = b(b^{-1}a)\,b^{-1},$$

if $b^{-1}\,a \in S$, then $ab^{-1} \in S$, which completes the proof.

(2) $a < b$, or $a = b$, or $b < a$.

Proof. From the decomposition (2.1) of G, we have that either $ab^{-1} \in S$, and then $a < b$, or $ab^{-1} \in \{1\}$, and then $a = b$, or $ab^{-1} \in S^{-1}$, and then $ba^{-1} \in S$, and $b < a$.

If $a < b$ or $a = b$, we write $a \leqslant b$, or $b \geqslant a$.

(3)   If $a < b$, and $c \in G$, then $ac < bc$, and $ca < cb$.

Proof. Since $a < b$, $ab^{-1} \in S$, so

$$acc^{-1}b^{-1} \in S, \qquad \text{i.e.,} \qquad (ac)\,(bc)^{-1} \in S,$$

which means that $ac < bc$. Similarly, one shows that $ca < cb$.

(4)   If $a < b$, and $b < c$, then $a < c$.

Proof. Since $a < b$, $ab^{-1} \in S$. Also, since $b < c$, $bc^{-1} \in S$. Therefore

$$ac^{-1} = (ab^{-1})\,(bc^{-1}) \in S,$$

for S is a semigroup, so a $< c$.

(5)   If $a < b$, then $b^{-1} < a^{-1}$.

Proof. By property (3), $a < b$ implies that $1 < a^{-1}b$, and this implies, again by (3); that $b^{-1} < a^{-1}$.

(6)   If $a < b$, and $c < d$, then $ac < bd$.

Proof. From $a < b$, we get, using (3), that $ac < bc$. Similarly, $bc < bd$, and then, by (4), $ac < bd$.

In an ordered group G, it is possible that an additive operation

$(+)$ is also defined. However, it is always possible to introduce in G an additive operation by defining

$$a + b = \max(a, b), \qquad (2.3)$$

which is well defined by property (2). Also, the operation $+$ is clearly an associative operation. It can also be seen that the distributive laws are satisfied. For example, suppose $a \leqslant b$, then $ac \leqslant bc$, and $\max(ac, bc) = bc$. However, $\max(a, b) c = bc$. Therefore $ac + bc = (a + b) c$.

Next, if G is an ordered group, we shall adjoin a zero element, i.e., form $G \cup \{0\}$, in such a way that $a \cdot 0 = 0 \cdot a = 0$ for all $a \in G$, and such that $0 < a$ for all $a \in G$. Then, by (2.3),

$$a + 0 = 0 + a = a,$$

for any $a \in G$.

With these notions, we can now give the definition of a valuation.

Definition 2.2.   A valuation of a field K is a map $| \ |$: $K \to G \cup \{0\}$, where G is an ordered group provided

(1)   for $a \in K$, $| a | = 0$ if and only if $a = 0$;

(2)   for $a, b \in K$, $| ab | = | a | | b |$;

(3) $| a + b | \leqslant | a | + | b |$.

It follows immediately from (2) of the definition that $| 1 | = 1$. We also have that $| -1 | = 1$, for, again by (2),

$$| -1 |^2 = | 1 | = 1;$$

however, in an ordered group, G, there exists no element except the identity with finite order, for if $a > 1$, then $a^n > 1$ for any positive integer n.

We now suppose that the additive operation in G is based on the max, i.e., it is given by (2.3); whence, condition (3) of the definition becomes

$$| a + b | \leqslant \max(| a |, | b |),$$

and the valuation is this case will be called *non-archimedian*.

Note that I, Theorem 2.2 also holds for our more general non-archimedian valuations. The proof is the same.

Next, we shall show that to a given nonarchimedian valuation there is an *associated* valuation ring. Let

$$V = \{a \in K \mid |a| \leqslant 1\}. \tag{2.4}$$

V is certainly a ring, for if $a, b \in V$, then $|a| \leqslant 1$ and $|b| \leqslant 1$, so

$$|ab| = |a||b| \leqslant 1, \tag{2.5}$$

and

$$|a - b| \leqslant \max(|a|, |b|) \leqslant 1. \tag{2.6}$$

Equations (2.5) and (2.6) imply that V is a ring. Next, let us show that V is a valuation ring. Thus, suppose that $a \notin V$. Then $|a| > 1$; therefore,

$$|a^{-1}| = |a|^{-1} < 1.$$

Hence, $a^{-1} \in V$, and V is, indeed, a valuation ring.

The non-units, P, of V are those $a \in V$ such that $a^{-1} \notin V$, or, in other words, those $a \in K$ such that $|a| \leqslant 1$ and $|a|^{-1} > 1$, so

$$P = \{a \in K \mid |a| < 1\}. \tag{2.7}$$

Consequently, the units, U, of V are

$$U = \{a \in K \mid |a| = 1\}. \tag{2.8}$$

Now, let us analyze a given valuation mapping $|\ |$ more carefully. Denote by K^* the set $K - \{0\}$. Condition (2) of Definition 2.2 states that $|\ |$ restricted to the multiplicative group K^* is a homomorphism into the group G. If we denote the image group by $|K^*|$ and observe, by (2.8), that the kernel of this homomorphism is precisely U, then we obtain

$$K^*/U \simeq |K^*|.$$

Thus we have that $|\ |$ on K^* factors into the product of the following sequence of mappings:

$$K^* \xrightarrow{\ \kappa\ } K^*/U \xrightarrow{\ f\ } |\ K^*\ | \xrightarrow{\ i\ } G \qquad (2.9)$$

where κ is the canonical map, f is an isomorphism, and i is the injection map.

Suppose we now reverse the procedure, namely, suppose a valuation ring, V, of a field K is given. Let P be the unique maximal ideal of non-units of V, and let U be the group of units of V. To the given valuation ring V, we wish to obtain an *associated* valuation. From the previous discussion, in particular from (2.9), the following map suggests itself:

$$|\ a\ | = \begin{cases} aU & \text{for} & a \in K^* \\ 0 & \text{for} & a = 0. \end{cases} \qquad (2.10)$$

Thus, we take $G = K^*/U$ and the additive operation in G based on the max. We must therefore, show first of all that G is an ordered group. To do this, we must exhibit a subsemigroup, S, with the required properties. Define S as follows: $aU \in S$ if and only if $a \in P^* = P - \{0\}$. Clearly S is a semigroup, and it is certainly normal since K is a field. Also, by (1.2) of this chapter,

$$K^* = P^* \cup U \cup (P^*)^{-1} \qquad \text{(disjoint)}.$$

Therefore, we get mod U that

$$G = K^*/U = S \cup \{1\} \cup S^{-1} \qquad \text{(disjoint)}$$

so $G = K^*/U$ is an ordered group.

Now, we check that $|\ a\ | = aU$ satisfies the conditions of Definition 2.2. The first two conditions follow immediately from the definition of $|\ a\ |$. To verify the third condition, we must show that $|\ a + b\ | \leqslant |\ a\ | + |\ b\ |$. However, this is equivalent to the following:

$$|\ a\ | \leqslant 1 \Rightarrow |\ 1 + a\ | \leqslant 1 + |\ a\ |. \qquad (2.11)$$

For, say, $| a/b | \leqslant 1$, then, if (2.11) is satisfied,

$$\left| 1 + \frac{a}{b} \right| \leqslant 1 + \left| \frac{a}{b} \right|,$$

which implies that $| a + b | \leqslant | a | + | b |$. However, condition (3) certainly implies (2.11). Therefore, in our case, in which the addition is based on the max, we must show that $| a | \leqslant 1$ implies that $| 1 + a | \leqslant 1$. Thus, suppose that $aU = | a | \leqslant 1$. Then $a \in V$, and, therefore, $1 + a \in V$, i.e., $| 1 + a | \leqslant 1$. Hence, $| a | = aU$ is a valuation and, moreover, its associated valuation ring is the given one V.

Summarizing, we have that a given valuation determines an associated valuation ring, which, in turn, determines an associated valuation, which is equal to the given valuation up to an ismorphism. If we define two valuations as *equivalent* if they have the same associated valuation ring (this, incidentally, is consistent with our use of the word equivalent for rank 1 valuations in Chapter I), then we can say that there is a one-to-one correspondence between non-archimedian valuations and valuation rings up to an equivalency. Since we have already seen that there is a one-to-one correspondence between places and valuation rings up to an equivalency, we now have the complete interconnection of the three concepts, and, by identifying equivalent places and equivalent valuations, we have that there is a one-to-one correspondence between places, valuation rings, and non-archimedian valuations. In the sequel, we shall not distinguish equivalent places or equivalent valuations.

Let us pause for a moment and consider a specific example. We take $K = C(z)$. The field of all rational functions of a single complex variable. We know that a place is obtained by substituting $z_0 \in C$ for z. The associated valuation ring of this place is

$$V = \left\{ \frac{f(z)}{g(z)} \,\Big|\, g(z_0) \neq 0 \right\},$$

where $f(z), g(z) \in C[z]$. The maximal ideal of non-units is

$$P = \left\{ \frac{f(z)}{g(z)} \,\Big|\, g(z_0) \neq 0, f(z_0) = 0 \right\},$$

and, finally, the group of units is

$$U = \left\{ \frac{f(z)}{g(z)} \,\middle|\, g(z_0) \neq 0, f(z_0) \neq 0 \right\},$$

The valuation associated with this valuation ring is

$$|\, h(z)\,| = h(z)\, U,$$

where $h(z) \in C(z)$. Hence

$$|\, h(z)\,| = (z - z_0)^n\, U,$$

and n is called the order of the zero of $h(z)$ at z_0 if $n \geqslant 0$, and $-n$ the order of the pole of $h(z)$ at z_0 if $n < 0$.

The ordered group G here is just the infinite cyclic group generated by $(z - z_0)\, U$, and is, therefore, isomorphic to Z. Finally, we have

$$|\, h(z)\,| < 1 \Leftrightarrow (z - z_0)^n \in P^* \Leftrightarrow n > 0.$$

We see that the given place merely tells us if a function has a pole or zero at a given point z_0, while the valuation gives us a refinement of this statement by telling us about the order of the pole or zero.

3. Valuations of General Rank

We want to consider specifically how the non-archimedian valuations of rank 1, considered in Chapters I and II, fit into the general scheme of things discussed in the previous section of this chapter. In order to do this, we must introduce a general notion of *rank* of a non-archimedian valuation, and show that for the non-archimedian valuations of rank 1 the general value group can always be replaced by an additive subgroup of the field R of real numbers which is order-isomorphic to it.

In order to carry out this program, we must introduce some preliminary notions. Let G be an ordered group as defined in Definition 2.1 of the previous section. We shall assume throughout that $G \neq 1$.

Definition 3.1. A subgroup H of G, where G is an ordered group, is called *isolated* if $b \in H$, and $b^{-1} \leqslant a \leqslant b$, where $a \in G$, imply $a \in H$.

Clearly, the whole group G and the identity subgroup, $\{1\}$, are isolated subgroups of G. It is entirely possible that these are the only isolated subgroups of G. This occurs, for example, when G is infinite cyclic.

We shall now prove the following fundamental fact.

Theorem 3.1. If H_1 and H_2 are two isolated subgroups of the ordered group G, then either $H_1 \subset H_2$ or $H_2 \subset H_1$.

Proof. Let $S_1 = \{a \in H_1 \mid a > 1\}$, and $S_2 = \{a \in H_2 \mid a > 1\}$. We first note that, if $H_1 \neq H_2$, $S_1 \neq S_2$, for suppose $S_1 = S_2$. Let $a \in H_1$. If $a > 1$, then $a \in S_1 = S_2 \subset H_2$. If $a < 1$, then $a^{-1} > 1$, which implies $a^{-1} \in S_1 = S_2 \subset H_2$, and, therefore, $a \in H_2$. Thus $H_1 \subset H_2$. Similarly, $H_2 \subset H_1$, and $H_1 = H_2$, which contradicts the assumption. Thus, if $H_1 \neq H_2$, $S_1 \neq S_2$, and we may find, say, an element $a \in H_1$, $a > 1$, and $a \notin H_2$. Let $b \in S_2$. Now, we must have $b < a$, for, otherwise, $b^{-1} \leqslant a \leqslant b$, which would imply that $a \in H_2$ since $b \in H_2$ and since H_2 is isolated. Thus $b < a$, but $b > 1 > a^{-1}$. Hence,

$$a^{-1} < b < a.$$

where a belongs to the isolated subgroup H_1. Thus, $b \in H_1$, and we have shown that $S_2 \subset H_1$, but this clearly implies that $H_2 \subset H_1$.

Theorem 3.1 shows that the set of all isolated subgroups of an ordered group G form a totally ordered set with respect to the order relation given by set inclusion.

Definition 3.2. Let G be an ordered group. The order type of the set of all isolated subgroups of G distinct from G is called the *rank* of G.

Definition 3.3. If $\mid \mid$ is a non-archimedian valuation of a field K into $G \cup \{0\}$, where G is an ordered group, then the *rank* of $\mid \mid$ is the rank of G.

Definition 3.4. Two ordered groups G and G' are called *order-isomorphic* if there exists an isomorphism: $a \rightarrow a'$ mapping G onto G' such that $a < b \Rightarrow a' < b'$, where $a, b \in G$, $a', b' \in G'$.

As our last definition of this section, we have:

Definition 3.5. An ordered group G is called *archimedian* if for every $a, b \in G$ with $b > 1$, there exists an integer n such that $b^n > a$.

Let us consider some relationships between, and consequences of, these definitions.

Theorem 3.2. An ordered group G is of rank 1 if and only if it is archimedian.

Proof. (1) We suppose first that the rank of G is one. If G is not archimedian, then there exist elements $a, b \in G$ such that $b > a > 1$, and $a^n > b$ does not hold for any positive integer n. Let

$$S = \{c \in G \mid 1 < c, \quad \text{and} \quad c < a^n \text{ for some } n\}.$$

Clearly, $b \notin S$. If c_1 and c_2 belong to S, say, $1 < c_1 < a^n$ and $1 < c_2 < a^m$, then

$$1 < c_1 c_2 < a^{n+m},$$

and $c_1 c_2 \in S$. Hence, S is a subsemigroup. Also, if $1 < d < c$, where $c \in S$, then $d \in S$. Now let $H = [S]$, be the subgroup of G generated by S. Since S is a semigroup, H is the set of all elements of the form

$$c_1{}^{\epsilon_1} c_2{}^{\epsilon_2} \cdots c_n{}^{\epsilon_n}$$

where the $c_i \in S$, and the $\epsilon_i = \pm 1$. We claim that H is an isolated subgroup of G distinct from $\{1\}$ and G. Once this has been shown, the first part of the theorem will have been established, for this would contradict the fact that the rank of G is 1, and, hence, the assumption that G is not archimedian is false.

Now, clearly, $H \neq \{1\}$ since $a \in H$. Next, $H \neq G$, for $b \notin H$, namely, if

$$b = c_1{}^{\epsilon_1} c_2{}^{\epsilon_2} \cdots c_n{}^{\epsilon_n} \tag{3.1}$$

where the $c_i \in S$, and the $\epsilon_i = \pm 1$, then for those c_i with $\epsilon_i = -1$, $c_i^{\epsilon_i} < 1$, and for those c_j with $\epsilon_j = 1$, $c_j^{\epsilon_j} < a^{n_j}$ for some n_j. Hence, (3.1) implies that

$$b < a^{\Sigma_j n_j},$$

where the summation is over those j with $\epsilon_j = 1$ in (3.1), but this means that $b \in S$, which is a contradiction. Finally, H is isolated for suppose $e \in H$, and $e^{-1} \leqslant d \leqslant e$, where $d \in G$. Then, if $e = c_1^{\epsilon_1} c_2^{\epsilon_2} \cdots c_n^{\epsilon_n}$, we have

$$c_n^{-\epsilon_n} \cdots c_1^{-\epsilon_1} \leqslant d \leqslant c_1^{\epsilon_1} \cdots c_n^{\epsilon_n}, \qquad (3.2)$$

but, as in the argument above,

$$d \leqslant c_1^{\epsilon_1} \cdots c_n^{\epsilon_n}$$

implies that $d < a^m$, for some integer m. If $d > 1$, then $d \in S \subset H$. If $d < 1$, then $d^{-1} > 1$, and, by (3.2),

$$c_1^{\epsilon_1} \cdots c_n^{\epsilon_n} \geqslant d^{-1}$$

whence, as before, $d^{-1} \in S \subset H$, and $d \in H$. This completes the proof of the first part of the theorem.

(2) Conversely, suppose that G is archimedian. Let H be an isolated subgroup of G where $H \neq \{1\}$. Choose $b \in H$, where $b > 1$. Let a be an arbitrary element of G, and say, $a > 1$. Then there exists an integer n such that $b^n > a$; whence,

$$b^{-n} < a < b^n,$$

and $a \in H$. If $a < 1$, then $a^{-1} > 1$, and, by the preceding result, $a^{-1} \in H$, so $a \in H$. Thus $H = G$, and the rank of G is 1. The theorem has now been established.

The next consequence of the definitions that we shall establish is the following:

Theorem 3.3. An archimedian ordered group G is abelian.

Proof. If we can show that for any two elements a, $b \in G$, where $a > 1$ and $b > 1$, $ab = ba$, then we are clearly done.

Suppose, first that there exists a smallest element $c \in G$ such that $c > 1$. If $a > 1$, then, by definition of c, $c \leqslant a$. Also, since G is archimedian, there exists a positive integer n such that

$$c^n \leqslant a < c^{n+1}.$$

Thus, $1 \leqslant ac^{-n} < c$, which implies that $ac^{-n} = 1$, or $a = c^n$. Thus, if $a > 1$, $a = c^n$ for some positive integer n. If $a < 1$, then $a^{-1} > 1$, and $a^{-1} = c^m$ for some positive integer m, and $a = c^{-m}$. Therefore, in this case, $G = [c]$, the infinite cyclic group generated by c, and G is, of course, abelian.

Next, we suppose that there exists no smallest element of G greater than 1. We shall first show that if c is any element of G such that $c > 1$, there exists an element $d \in G$, where $1 < d < c$, and $d^2 \leqslant c$. Since $c > 1$, and since G contains no smallest element greater than 1, there exists an element $e \in G$ such that

$$1 < e < c. \tag{3.3}$$

There are two possibilities: either $e^2 \leqslant c$, or $e^2 > c$. In the first case, we take $d = e$ as the desired element. Let us consider now the second case.

$$e^2 > c \tag{3.4}$$

and, therefore, $e > ce^{-1}$. Thus, $1 > e^{-1}ce^{-1}$, and

$$c > ce^{-1}ce^{-1} = (ce^{-1})^2. \tag{3.5}$$

Take $d = ce^{-1}$. Then, by (3.5), we have $c > d^2$, and, using (3.3) and (3.4), we have

$$1 < d = ce^{-1} < e < c,$$

and $d = ce^{-1}$ is the desired element.

Now, suppose that $a, b \in G$, where $a > 1$ and $b > 1$. Suppose $ab \neq ba$. There is no loss of generality in assuming

$$ab(ba)^{-1} = c > 1.$$

Then, by the preceding result together with the fact that G contains no smallest element greater than 1, we can find a $d \in G$, where

$$1 < d < c, \quad d^2 \leqslant c \quad \text{and} \quad d < a, \quad d < b.$$

Since G is archimedian, there exist positive integers m and n such that

$$d^m \leqslant a < d^{m+1} \quad \text{and} \quad d^n \leqslant b < d^{n+1}.$$

Therefore,

$$d^{m+n} \leqslant ab < d^{m+n+2}, \quad \text{and} \quad d^{-(m+n+2)} < (ba)^{-1} \leqslant d^{-(m+n)}.$$

Thus

$$d^{-2} < (ab)(ba)^{-1} < d^2, \quad \text{or} \quad d^{-2} < c < d^2 \leqslant c,$$

a contradiction. This completes the proof of the theorem.

Finally, we establish the following theorem, which will show how the valuations of rank one considered in Chapters I and II fit into the general concepts of this chapter.

Theorem 3.4. An ordered group G of rank 1 is order-isomorphic to a subgroup of the additive group R of real numbers.

Proof. By Theorems 3.2 and 3.3, we know that G is abelian. If G contains a smallest element c such that $c > 1$, then, as seen in the first part of the proof of Theorem 3.3, $G = [c]$, and, therefore, G can be mapped in an order-ismorphic fashion onto Z, the additive group of integers.

Next, suppose that there exists no smallest element of G greater than 1. First, we map the identity, 1, of G into the real number 0. Next, let a be an arbitrary element of G with $a > 1$. We map a into the real number 1. Now, let $b \in G$; to b we associate a real number b' defined as follows: for $m/n \in Q$, with $n > 0$, $m/n \in L(b)$, the lower class of a Dedekind cut b', if $a^m \leqslant b^n$, and $m/n \in U(b)$, the upper class of a Dedekind cut b' if $a^m > b^n$. Clearly $m/n \in L(b)$ or $m/n \in U(b)$. Since G is archimedian, $b^{-n} < a < b^n$ for some integer n. If n is positive $1/n \in L(b)$; also, there exists an m such that $a^m > b^n$, so $m/n \in U(b)$. Thus $L(b) \neq \emptyset$ and $U(b) \neq \emptyset$. A similar argument establishes the same result if n is negative.

If $m/n \in U(b)$, and if $s/t \geqslant m/n$, where n, $t > 0$, then $ns \geqslant mt$. Thus, since $a^m > b^n$, we have $a^{ns} \geqslant a^{mt} > b^{nt}$; whence, $a^s > b^t$, and $s/t \in U(b)$. It now follows that $L(b)$ and $U(b)$ are indeed, the lower and upper classes of a Dedekind cut, b', in R.

Suppose that b, $c \in G$ and $b > c$. Then $bc^{-1} > 1$, and, by the archimedian property of G, there exists a positive integer n such that

$$(bc^{-1})^n > a, \qquad \text{or} \qquad b^n > ac^n. \qquad (3.6)$$

Let m be the smallest integer such that $a^m > c^n$. For this m, we must have

$$b^n \geqslant a^m > c^n, \qquad (3.7)$$

since, otherwise, $a^m > b^n$, which implies, by (3.6), that $a^m > ac^n$, and then $a^{m-1} > c^n$. This, however, contradicts the choice of m. Hence, (3.7) holds, and this implies that $m/n \in L(b)$, and $m/n \in U(c)$; whence $b' > c'$, and our correspondence is one-one and preserves the ordering.

If $m_1/n_1 \in L(b)$ and $m_2/n_2 \in L(c)$, then we can write $m_1/n_1 = m/n$, and $m_2/n_2 = m'/n$. We have

$$a^m \leqslant b^n, \qquad \text{and} \qquad a^{m'} \leqslant c^n.$$

Thus, $a^{m+m'} \leqslant (bc)^n$, so

$$\frac{m}{n} + \frac{m'}{n} = \frac{m + m'}{n} \in L(bc).$$

Therefore, we have shown that

$$L(b) + L(c) \subset L(bc).$$

Similarly,

$$U(b) + U(c) \subset U(bc),$$

and from these relations it follows immediately that $(bc)' = b' + c'$, and the proof of the theorem has been completed.

Thus in considering valuations of rank 1, we may always assume that the ordered group G is a subgroup of the additive group of real numbers with the customary ordering. These were the type valuations considered in Chapters I and II, and the reason for the rank one terminology initially adopted there is now clear.

4. The Extension Theorem

We shall now establish the fundamental extension theorem for places, which will play a basic role in the subsequent discussion on the extension of non-archimedian valuations. In the hypothesis of the theorem, it will be assumed that a certain field, F, is algebraically closed. This is no real restriction since, in general, one could always inject F into its algebraic closure. We now state and prove the theorem.

Theorem 4.1.   Let K be a field and A a subring of K. Let F be an algebraically closed field, and

$$f : A \to F,$$

a nontrivial homomorphism. Then there exists a place ϕ of K such that $\phi \mid_A = f$, where $\phi \mid_A$ is the restriction of ϕ to A.

Proof.   Let

$$S = \{b \in A \mid f(b) \neq 0\}.$$

It is clear that S is a semigroup and that $S \neq \theta$ since f is nontrivial. We form the quotient ring

$$A' = \left\{ \frac{a}{b} \mid a \in A,\, b \in S \right\}.$$

A' is a ring with identity which contains A as a subring, and in A' all elements of S have inverses. We shall now extend f to a mapping f' defined on A'. This is done as follows: for $a/b \in A'$ define

$$f'\left(\frac{a}{b}\right) = \frac{f(a)}{f(b)}.$$

We first observe that the map f' is well defined, for if $a_1/b_1 = a_2/b_2$, where a_1, $a_2 \in A$, and b_1, $b_2 \in S$, then $a_1 b_2 = a_2 b_1$, and since f is a homomorphism

$$f(a_1) f(b_2) = f(a_2) f(b_1).$$

However, $f(b_1) \neq 0$ and $f(b_2) \neq 0$. Thus, dividing by $f(b_1) f(b_2)$ we get

$$\frac{f(a_1)}{f(b_1)} = \frac{f(a_2)}{f(b_2)},$$

which shows that f' is well defined. It follows immediately from (4.1) that f' is a homomorphism since f is. Also, $f'|_A = f$, for if $a \in A$, then $a = ab/b$, where $b \in S$, and

$$f'\left(\frac{ab}{b}\right) = \frac{f(ab)}{f(b)} = \frac{f(a)f(b)}{f(b)} = f(a).$$

This is the first type of extension, but it is possible that it yields no extension at all. This will be the case when the ring A is its own quotient ring, i.e., when $a \in A$ and $f(a) \neq 0$ implies that $a^{-1} \in A$. When this occurs, we shall show that if we select any $\alpha \in K$, f can be extended to either the ring $A[\alpha]$ or to the ring $A[\alpha^{-1}]$, and this is the second type of extension that we shall consider.

Thus, assume that A is its own quotient ring. We first note that $f(A) = F_0$ is a subfield of F, for let $c_0 \in F_0$ and $c_0 \neq 0$. Then $c_0 = f(a) \neq 0$, where $a \in A$. Hence, $a^{-1} \in A$, and

$$1 = f(aa^{-1}) = f(a)f(a^{-1}) = c_0 f(a^{-1});$$

Therefore, c_0 has an inverse in F_0, and F_0 is a field.

We shall denote by $\bar{a}$, the image of $a \in A$ under the homomorphism f. We extend f to the polynomial ring $A[x]$ in a transcendental element x in the obvious fashion by just applying f to the coefficients of a polynomial. The image of $P(x) \in A[x]$ will be denoted by $\bar{P}(x)$. The image of $A[x]$ under this extended homomorphism is just $F_0[x]$, and $F_0[x]$ is a principal ideal domain since F_0 is a field. Now we attempt to extend f to a homomorphism g on $A[\alpha]$, where $\alpha \in K$, by defining

$$g(P(\alpha)) = \bar{P}(\beta), \qquad (4.2)$$

where β is any element of F. If g is well defined, then it is certainly a homomorphism which extends f. Thus, we must just see if g is well defined. This amounts to showing that $P(\alpha) = 0$ implies $\bar{P}(\beta) = 0$. Let

$$I = \{P(x) \in A[x] \mid P(\alpha) = 0\}.$$

I is clearly the kernel of the substitution map:

$$A[x] \twoheadrightarrow A[\alpha],$$

and is, therefore, an ideal of $A[x]$. Hence, to check if g is well defined, we must determine whether the image $\bar{I}$ in $F_0[x]$ of I is such that $x = \beta$ is a zero of it, i.e., whether $\bar{P}(\beta) = 0$ for all $\bar{P}(x) \in \bar{I}$. If this is the case, then g is clearly well defined. Since $\bar{I}$ is an ideal of $F_0[x]$, $\bar{I}$ is a principal ideal, and we have

$$\bar{I} = \bar{Q}(x) \cdot F_0[x],$$

for some $\bar{Q}(x) \in F_0[x]$. Thus β must be selected so that $\bar{Q}(\beta) = 0$, and, since F is algebraically closed, such a β can be chosen provided $\bar{Q}(x)$ is not a nonzero constant polynomial. Hence, if $\bar{Q}(x)$ is not a nonzero constant polynomial, we have an extension of f to g given by (4.2) on $A[\alpha]$. However, it is possible that $\bar{Q}(x)$ is a nonzero constant (should $\bar{Q}(x) = 0$, then it is clear that any $\beta \in F$ may be chosen), in which case our construction fails. Thus, we must consider this case in more detail.

Clearly, we may assume that $\bar{Q}(x) = 1$. Then there is a

$$Q(x) = 1 + a_0 + a_1 x + \cdots + a_t x^t,$$

where $\bar{a}_i = 0$, $i = 0, 1, ..., t$, and where

$$1 + a_0 + a_1 \alpha + \cdots + a_t \alpha^t = 0.$$

Thus, if α satisfies such an equation, our construction does not go through. However, we shall now show that if this situation prevails, then we can extend f to $A[\alpha^{-1}]$. For suppose the construction did not work for $A[\alpha]$ and for $A[\alpha^{-1}]$. Then we would have

$$1 + a_0 + a_1\alpha + \cdots + a_t\alpha^t = 0. \tag{4.3}$$

and

$$1 + a_0' + a_1'\frac{1}{\alpha} + \cdots + a_s'\frac{1}{\alpha^s} = 0, \tag{4.4}$$

where the a_i and a_i' belong to A, and where $\bar{a}_i = \bar{a}_j' = 0$, $i = 0, ..., t, j = 0, ..., s$.

We may also assume that t and s are the minimal degrees of such equations satisfied by α and $1/\alpha$, and we may also assume that $s \leq t$ since the argument will be symmetric in s and t. Observe, first, that both t and s are greater than or equal 1, for if, e.g., $t = 0$, then

$$1 + a_0 = 0,$$

and this implies that

$$\bar{1} + \bar{a}_0 = 0,$$

or $\bar{1} = 0$, since $\bar{a}_0 = 0$. However, this is a contradiction since f is nontrivial. Next, from (4.4), one gets

$$\alpha^s = \frac{-a_1'}{1 + a_0'}\alpha^{s-1} - \cdots - \frac{a_s'}{1 + a_0'}. \tag{4.5}$$

The coefficients of (4.5) belong to A since $\bar{1} + \bar{a}_0' = \bar{1} \neq 0$, and A is its own quotient ring. Thus, (4.5) can be written as

$$\alpha^s = a_0'' + a_1''\alpha + \cdots + a_{s-1}''\alpha^{s-1}, \tag{4.6}$$

where the $a_i'' \in A$, and where $\bar{a}_i'' = 0, i = 0, ..., s - 1$. Since $s \leqslant t$, we can write

$$\alpha^t = \alpha^s(\alpha^{t-s}),$$

where $t - s \geqslant 0$. Now, using (4.6), we can lower the degree of α in (4.3), i.e., we can write (4.3) as

$$1 + a_0 + a_1\alpha + \cdots + a_t(\alpha^{t-s})\,\alpha^s = 0,$$

or

$$1 + a_0 + a_1\alpha + \cdots + a_t\alpha^{t-s}(a_0'' + a_1''\alpha + \cdots + a_{s-1}''\alpha^{s-1}) = 0, \tag{4.7}$$

and the highest power of α in (4.7) is $t - 1$, which contradicts the minimality of t. Hence, we have finally shown that if we can not extend f to $A[\alpha]$, we can extend it to $A[\alpha^{-1}]$.

We are now in a position to apply Zorn's lemma. Let E denote the set of all extensions of f to larger rings. In other words, $g \in E$ if g is a homomorphism defined on a ring $B \supset A$, and $g \mid_A = f$. If g_1, $g_2 \in E$, we define $g_2 > g_1$, if g_2 is an extension of g_1. This clearly defines a partial ordering of E. Let $\{g_\alpha\}$ be any totally ordered subset of E. The set of rings, $\{A_\alpha\}$, on which the g_α are defined are, therefore, totally ordered by ordinary set inclusion. Form the union of these rings, which is a ring in this case and define g on this union as follows: if $a \in \bigcup_\alpha A_\alpha$, then a belongs to one of the rings, say A_α, and define

$$g(a) = g_\alpha(a).$$

g is well defined since the set $\{g_\alpha\}$ is totally ordered, and g is clearly a homomorphism. It is also clear that $g > g_\alpha$ for all α, and $g \in E$. Thus, the set E is inductively ordered, and, therefore, has a maximal element. Let h be such a maximal element, and

$$h: \quad V \to F.$$

Since h can not be extended any further, we know, by the preceding discussion, that

(1) V is its own quotient ring by elements with nonzero images, i.e., if $a \in V$, and if $h(a) \neq 0$, then $a^{-1} \in V$;

(2) if $\alpha \notin V$, then we know that h cannot be extended to $V[\alpha]$ since h is a maximal element of E. However, this means, as we

previously saw, that h can then be extended to $V[\alpha^{-1}]$, but, since h is maximal, we must have $\alpha^{-1} \in V$. In other words, if $\alpha \notin V$, then $\alpha^{-1} \in V$, or V is a valuation ring.

Finally we show that the place, ϕ, associated with this valuation ring is equal to h up to an isomorphism. This follows from (1), for by (1), if $a \in V$ and if $h(a) \neq 0$, then $a^{-1} \in V$. Conversely, if if $a \in V$ and if $a^{-1} \in V$, then $h(a) \neq 0$, for, otherwise,

$$h(1) = h(aa^{-1}) = h(a)\, h(a^{-1}) = 0,$$

which implies that h and, therefore, f is trivial. Hence, the kernel, P, of h is the set of non-units of V, and h decomposes into the product of the following maps:

$$V \xrightarrow{\kappa} V/P \xrightarrow{h'} h(V) \xrightarrow{i} F,$$

where κ is the canonical map, $h'(a + P) = h(a)$, and i the injection map. It is now clear that $h = \phi$ on V up to an isomorphism. We now extend h to all of K by mapping a into ∞ if $a \notin V$. Then $h = \phi$ up to an isomorphism, and the proof of the extension theorem has been completed.

5. Integral Closure

As mentioned before, our main application of the extension theorem will be to the extension of valuations. However, because of its importance in number theory, we shall digress in this section in order to give an application of the concepts introduced in this chapter and also of the extension theorem to the concept of integral closure.

Let A be a ring with an identity element and let A be a subring of the field K. We shall first give the customary definition of the integral closure of A in K, i.e., we shall give a definition not using the notion of places, and then shall show the relation of this concept to that of places.

Definition 5.1. An element $\alpha \in K$ is called *integral* over A if α satisfies an equation of the form

$$\alpha^n + a_1\alpha^{n-1} + \cdots + a_n = 0$$

where the $a_i \in A$. The totality of elements of K which are integral over A is called the *integral closure* of A in K.

Clearly any element of A is integral over A. If $A = Z$ and $K = C$, an element α which satisfies such an equation is called an *algebraic integer*.

We let S denote the set of all places of K which are finite on A, i.e., S is the set of all places of K whose associated valuation rings contain A.

Theorem 5.1. If $\alpha \in K$ is integral over A, and if $\phi \in S$, then ϕ is finite on α.

Proof. Suppose $\phi(\alpha) = \infty$. Then $\phi(1/\alpha) = 0$.
However, α satisfies the equation

$$\alpha^n + a_1\alpha^{n-1} + \cdots + a_n = 0,$$

where the $a_i \in A$. Divide by α^n; then

$$1 + a_1\frac{1}{\alpha} + \cdots a_n\frac{1}{\alpha^n} = 0,$$

and apply the place ϕ to this. We then have

$$\phi(1) = 0,$$

a contradiction.

The theorem states that any place of K which is finite on A is finite on any element of K which is integral over A. We shall now establish the converse of this theorem. Actually, we shall prove a slightly stronger theorem.

Denote by S_0 the set of those places $\phi \in S$ whose kernel in A is a maximal ideal of A.

Theorem 5.2. Let $\alpha \in K$, and suppose $\phi(\alpha) \neq \infty$ for any $\phi \in S_0$. Then α is integral over A.

Proof. We note first of all that once the theorem has been proved it follows that $\phi(\alpha) \neq \infty$ for any $\phi \in S$ by Theorem 5.1. We now proceed to the proof.

If $\alpha = 0$, then $\alpha \in A$ and is, therefore, integral over A. Thus, we may assume that $\alpha \neq 0$. Consider the ring $A_1 = A[1/\alpha]$. The theorem will be proved if it can be shown that $1/\alpha$ is a unit of A_1, for this would imply that $\alpha \in A_1 = A[1/\alpha]$, which means that

$$\alpha = a_0 + a_1 \frac{1}{\alpha} + \cdots + a_t \frac{1}{\alpha^t}, \qquad (5.1)$$

where the $a_i \in A$. Multiplying (5.1) by α^t yields

$$\alpha^{t+1} - a_0 \alpha^t - \cdots - a_t = 0,$$

which implies that α is integral over A.

We shall now assume that $1/\alpha$ is not a unit of A_1 and shall arrive at a contradiction. If $1/\alpha$ is not a unit of A_1, then the principal ideal $(1/\alpha) A_1$ is not A_1. Thus, there exists (see appendix) a maximal ideal M of A_1 such that

$$\frac{1}{\alpha} A_1 \subset M.$$

Let us consider the canonical map

$$A_1 \to A_1/M.$$

Since M is maximal, A_1/M is a field, which we can inject into its algebraic closure. In this fashion, we obtain a homomorphic mapping of the ring A_1 into an algebraically closed field. Moreover, the homomorphism is nontrivial since $M \neq A_1$. By the extension theorem of the preceding section, we can extend this homomorphism to a place, ϕ, of K. Since ϕ is finite on A_1, it is finite on A. Therefore, $\phi \in S$. Now, $(1/\alpha) \in M$, so $\phi(1/\alpha) = 0$, and, consequently, $\phi(\alpha) = \infty$. This would already yield the desired contradiction had we used in the hypothesis of the theorem the set S instead of the set S_0. Thus, to complete the proof, we must just show that $\phi \in S_0$.

The kernel of ϕ in A_1 is, of course, M which is a maximal ideal of A_1. The kernel of ϕ in A is $A \cap M = N$, and we must just show that N is a maximal ideal of A in order to establish that $\phi \in S_0$.

We shall show that N is maximal by showing that A/N is a field (see appendix). Thus, suppose that $a \in A$ and that $a \notin N$. Then $a \in A_1$, and $a \notin M$. Since M is a maximal ideal of A_1 and since $a \notin M$, a must have an inverse in A_1 modulo M, i.e.,

$$a \left(b_0 + b_1 \frac{1}{\alpha} + \cdots + b_s \frac{1}{\alpha^s}\right) \equiv 1 \qquad (\text{mod } M), \qquad (5.2)$$

where the $b_i \in A$. However, $1/\alpha \equiv 0 \ (\text{mod } M)$, so (5.2) reduces to

$$ab_0 \equiv 1 \qquad (\text{mod } M),$$

i.e., $ab_0 - 1 \in M$, but, clearly, $ab_0 - 1 \in A$; whence, $ab_0 - 1 \in N$. Thus,

$$ab_0 \equiv 1 \qquad (\text{mod } N),$$

where $b_0 \in A$. This shows that A/N is a field and completes the proof of the theorem.

It follows immediately from Theorems 5.1 and 5.2 that the integral closure, $\bar{A}$, of A in K is a ring, for $\bar{A}$ is precisely the set of elements of K which are finite on all places of S.

Next, we show that the word "closure" is justified, i.e., we wish to show that the integral closure of $\bar{A}$ in K is precisely $\bar{A}$. Let $\tilde{S}$ denote the set of all places of K which are finite on $\bar{A}$. If $\phi \in \tilde{S}$, then, by definition, ϕ is finite on $\bar{A}$, and, therefore, on A, so $\phi \in S$. Conversely, if $\phi \in S$, then ϕ is finite on $\bar{A}$ since $\bar{A}$ is the integral closure of A. Thus, $\phi \in \tilde{S}$, and we have $S = \tilde{S}$. To see, therefore, if an element belongs to the integral closure of $\bar{A}$ in K, we must see if it is finite on any $\phi \in S$. It follows immediately that the integral closure of $\bar{A}$ in K is $\bar{A}$.

Finally, we note, in view of our characterization of the integral closure by means of places of S and by the interconnection between places and valuation rings, that $\bar{A}$, the integral closure of A in K, can be expressed as follows:

$$\bar{A} = \cap V,$$

where the intersection is taken over all valuation rings of K which contain A.

CHAPTER IV

Normed Linear Spaces

1. Basic Properties of Normed Linear Spaces

This chapter will be devoted to certain concepts and results mainly from analysis which, in conjunction with the results of the previous chapter, will enable us to tell the complete story on the extension of valuations. It is possible to proceed in a spirit much more algebraic and elementary in nature. For example, instead of introducing Banach algebras and giving an analytic proof of the Gel'fand theorem, we could instead present the elementary proof, due to Tornheim [20], that the only normed field over the real numbers, R, is either R itself or C, or we could present the more special result of Ostrowski [17]. We choose the present mode of treatment because it affords us an opportunity to present to the reader a number of concepts which play an extremely important role in mathematics today, which happen to have applications to the specific problems we are concerned with, but have many deep and beautiful applications far beyond the narrow use we shall make of them.

We first give a rather general definition of a normed linear space.

Definition 1.1. Let k be a field with a rank one valuation $|\ |$. Let X be a linear (vector) space over k. X is called a *normed linear space* over k if there exists a mapping, $\|\ \|$, called *norm*, where

$$\|\ \| : X \to R,$$

and is such that

(a) For $x \in X$, $\|x\| \geqslant 0$ and $= 0$ if and only if $x = 0$;

(b) for $x \in X$ and $\alpha \in k$, $\|\alpha x\| = |\alpha|\,\|x\|$;

(c) for $x, y \in X$, $\|x + y\| \leqslant \|x\| + \|y\|$.

To avoid special cases in the sequel, we shall always assume that $X \neq \{0\}$. The case $X = \{0\}$ is always trivial to handle.

Before considering some basic consequences of the definition, we shall consider a number of examples.

(1) Take $X = k = Q$ with the usual absolute value on Q as the valuation and as the norm.

(2) Take $X = Q_p$, $k = Q$ with the p-adic valuation as the valuation on Q and its extension to Q_p as the norm on X.

(3) Take $X = C[a, b]$, the set of all real valued continuous functions on the closed interval $[a, b]$. Let $k = R$, with the usual absolute value, and define, for $x \in X$, $\| x \| = \max_{t \in [a,b]} | x(t) |$.

(4) Take $X = C^n$, complex euclidean n-space. Let $k = C$ with the usual absolute value, and define, for $x = (\alpha_1, \alpha_2, ..., \alpha_n) \in C^n$,

$$\| x \| = (| \alpha_1 |^2 + \cdots + | \alpha_n |^2)^{1/2}.$$

The verification of the conditions (a), (b), (c) of Definition 1.1 in all the examples is quite direct and will be left to the reader.

Let X be a normed linear space. For $x, y \in X$, define

$$d(x, y) = \| x - y \|.$$

Clearly

(1) $d(x, y) \geqslant 0$ and equals 0 if and only if $x = y$;

(2) $d(x, y) = d(y, x)$,

since $\| x - y \| = \| -(y - x) \| = | -1 | \| y - x \| = \| y - x \|$;

(3) $d(x, z) \leqslant d(x, y) + d(y, z)$,

since $\| x - z \| = \| (x - y) + (y - z) \| \leqslant \| x - y \| + \| y - z \|$.

Thus X, d is a metric space, and we have that any normed linear space is a metric space, and consequently, a topological space. We can, therefore, introduce the customary topological concepts into such a space in terms of the metric. For example, the sequence $\{x_n\}$ of elements of X *converges* to $x \in X$, denoted by $x_n \rightarrow x$, if $d(x, x_n) \rightarrow 0$, or, in terms of the norm, if $\| x - x_n \| \rightarrow 0$. One can also speak of open and closed sets, compact sets, etc.

The notion of Cauchy sequences is introduced in the usual fashion, namely, the sequence $\{x_n\}$ of elements of X is called a *Cauchy sequence* if, for every real $\epsilon > 0$, there exists an integer, N, such that $d(x_n, x_m) < \epsilon$ for all $n, m > N$.

Finally, we note that one can also consider infinite series of elements in X.

Definition 1.2. If every Cauchy sequence of the normed linear space, X, converges to an element of X, then X is called a *Banach space*, or a *complete space*.

Examples (2), (3), and (4) are examples of Banach spaces, while (1) is not a Banach space.

We now draw some simple consequences from the definition of a normed linear space.

Theorem 1.1. Let X be a normed linear space. Then

(a) the operation of vector addition in X is continuous;

(b) the norm mapping is continuous.

Proof. Let $x, y, x_0, y_0 \in X$. Statement (a) follows immediately from the inequality

$$\| (x + y) - (x_0 + y_0) \| \leqslant \| x - x_0 \| + \| y - y_0 \|,$$

and statement (b) follows from the easily proved inequality

$$| \| x \| - \| x_0 \| | \leqslant \| x - x_0 \|.$$

Here, of course, the symbol $| \; |$ refers to the usual absolute value function on R.

Let X be a linear space, and suppose that $\| \; \|_1$ and $\| \; \|_2$ are two norms on X, i.e., two mappings of X into R which both satisfy the conditions of Definition 1.1.

Definition 1.3. The two norms $\| \; \|_1$ and $\| \; \|_2$ are *equivalent* if there exist two real numbers α, β both greater than 0 such that

$$\alpha \| x \|_1 \leqslant \| x \|_2 \leqslant \beta \| x \|_1$$

for all $x \in X$.

It is easy to see that this relation is an equivalence relation in the set of all norms defined on X. It is also not difficult to see that equivalent norms give rise to the same collection of open sets in X.

We now establish the following useful theorem.

Theorem 1.2.   Let X be a finite-dimensional linear space over a field k, where k is complete with respect to a rank one valuation, $|\ |$. Then any two norms on X are equivalent.

Proof.   We first define a very special norm on X. Let x_1, x_2, ..., x_n be a basis of X. Then, if $x \in X$, we can write x uniquely in the form

$$x = \sum_{i=1}^{n} \alpha_i x_i,$$

where the $\alpha_i \in k$. Define

$$\| x \|_0 = \max_i |\alpha_i|.$$

It is clear that $\|\ \|_0$ is a norm on X, and since the concept of equivalent norms is an equivalence relation, it suffices, in order to prove the theorem, to show that any norm, $\|\ \|$, on X is equivalent to $\|\ \|_0$.

Let $x \in X$, $x = \sum_{i=1}^{n} \alpha_i x_i$. Then

$$\| x \| = \left\| \sum_{i=1}^{n} \alpha_i x_i \right\|$$

$$\leqslant \sum_{i=1}^{n} |\alpha_i| \| x_i \|$$

$$\leqslant \| x \|_0 \sum_{i=1}^{n} \| x_i \|$$

$$= \beta \| x \|_0,$$

where $\beta = \sum_{i=1}^{n} \| x_i \| > 0$. Thus, to complete the proof, we must show that there exists a real number $\alpha > 0$ such that

$\alpha \| x \|_0 \leqslant \| x \|$. We shall establish this by induction on n, the dimension of X. If $n = 1$, let $x_1 \in X$, $x_1 \neq 0$. Then, for any $x \in X$, $x = \alpha_1 x_1$, $\alpha_1 \in k$, and

$$\| x \| = \| \alpha_1 x_1 \| = | \alpha_1 | \| x_1 \| = \| x \|_0 \| x_1 \| = \alpha \| x \|_0 \,,$$

where $\alpha = \| x_1 \|$. Hence, we are done in this case.

We assume now the inequality for all X of dimension $n - 1$, and consider X of dimension n. Let x_1, x_2, ..., x_n be a basis of X; also, let M be the subspace spanned by x_1, x_2, ..., x_{n-1}. The dimension of M is $n - 1$, so $\| \|$ and $\| \|_0$ are equivalent on M. Let y_1, y_2, ... be elements of M and be a Cauchy sequence with respect to $\| \|$. Then it is a Cauchy sequence with respect to $\| \|_0$. Write

$$y_i = \alpha_{1i} x_1 + \alpha_{2i} x_2 + \cdots + \alpha_{n-1 \, i} x_{n-1} \,, \qquad i = 1, 2, ...,$$

where the $\alpha_{ji} \in k$. The sequences $\{\alpha_{ji}\}$, $j = 1, ..., n - 1$ are Cauchy sequences in k since

$$| \alpha_{js} - \alpha_{jt} | \leqslant \| y_s - y_t \|_0 \,, \qquad j = 1, 2, ..., n - 1.$$

Therefore, by the completeness of k,

$$\lim_{i \to \infty} \alpha_{ji} = \alpha_j \in k \qquad \text{for} \qquad j = 1, ..., n - 1.$$

Set

$$y = \alpha_1 x_1 + \alpha_2 x_2 + \cdots + \alpha_{n-1} x_{n-1} \,.$$

Then it is clear that $y = \lim y_i$ in the norm $\| \|_0$ and, consequently, in the norm $\| \|$ since they are equivalent on M. Hence, M is complete. The metric space $x_n + M$ is isometric to M under the translation mapping: $x \to x_n + x$, and is, therefore, also complete. However, any complete subspace of a metric space is closed, so $x_n + M$ is closed in X, and its complement is, therefore, open. Now

$$0 \notin x_n + M,$$

for, otherwise,

$$0 = x_n + \beta_1 x_1 + \cdots + \beta_{n-1} x_{n-1} \,,$$

where the $\beta_i \in k$, which would contradict the fact that the x_i form a basis of X. Since $0 \notin x_n + M$, and since the complement is open, there exists a real number $\gamma_n > 0$ such that for $x \in x_n + M$

$$\| x \| = \| x - 0 \| \geqslant \gamma_n ,$$

i.e.,

$$\| \alpha_1 x_1 + \cdots + \alpha_{n-1} x_{n-1} + x_n \| \geqslant \gamma_n \qquad (1.1)$$

for arbitrary $\alpha_i \in k$. Let $x \in X$, and let

$$x = \alpha_1 x_1 + \alpha_2 x_2 + \cdots + \alpha_n x_n .$$

We claim that

$$\| x \| = \| \alpha_1 x_1 + \alpha_2 x_2 + \cdots + \alpha_n x_n \| \geqslant \gamma_n | \alpha_n | . \qquad (1.2)$$

Equation (1.2) is certainly true if $\alpha_n = 0$; while, if $\alpha_n \neq 0$, then we have from (1.1) that

$$\left\| \frac{\alpha_1}{\alpha_n} x_1 + \cdots + \frac{\alpha_{n-1}}{\alpha_n} x_{n-1} + x_n \right\| \geqslant \gamma_n ,$$

which yields (1.2) if we multiply both sides by $| \alpha_n |$.

Similarly, we get

$$\| x \| = \| \alpha_1 x_1 + \alpha_2 x_2 + \cdots + \alpha_n x_n \| \geqslant \gamma_i | \alpha_i | ,$$

$i = 1, ..., n$, and where each $\gamma_i > 0$. These other inequalities are obtained in an analogous fashion as (1.2) by considering the other $(n - 1)$-dimensional subspaces spanned by $n - 1$ basis vectors. Hence,

$$\| x \| = \| \alpha_1 x_1 + \cdots + \alpha_n x_n \| \geqslant \alpha \| x \|_0 ,$$

where $\alpha = \min_i \gamma_i > 0$, which completes the induction and establishes the theorem.

In the course of the proof, we established also the following result.

Theorem 1.3. If k is a complete field with respect to the rank one valuation $|\ |$, and if X is a finite-dimensional normed linear space over k, then X is also complete (i.e., X is a Banach space).

Although we shall not need it in the sequel, we note the following consequence of this theorem.

Corollary. If X is a normed linear space over the complete field k, any finite-dimensional subspace, M, of X is closed.

Proof. The norm, $\|\ \|$, on X restricted to M makes M a finite-dimensional normed linear space over the complete field k. M is, therefore, complete by Theorem 1.3, and, consequently, closed.

We note that the corollary is certainly not true for infinite-dimensional subspaces, namely, in Example (3) following Definition 1.1 take M to be the subspace of $C[a, b]$ consisting of all polynomials on $[a, b]$. M is clearly an infinite-dimensional subspace of $C[a, b]$, while $\bar{M}$, the closure of M, is $C[a, b]$ by the Weierstrass approximation theorem.

Definition 1.4. Let X be a normed linear space and let $\{x_n\}$ be a sequence of elements of X. The series $\sum_{n=1}^{\infty} x_n$ is called *absolutely convergent* if the series $\sum_{n=1}^{\infty} \|x_n\|$ converges.

For Banach spaces, we have the following result.

Theorem 1.4. If X is a Banach space, then any absolutely convergent series, $\sum_{n=1}^{\infty} x_n$, is convergent, and

$$\left\| \sum_{n=1}^{\infty} x_n \right\| \leqslant \sum_{n=1}^{\infty} \|x_n\|.$$

Proof. Let $\sum_{n=1}^{\infty} x_n$ be absolutely convergent. Then, for any $\epsilon > 0$, there exists an integer N such that for all $n \geqslant N$ and any $t \geqslant 0$

$$\|x_{n+1}\| + \cdots + \|x_{n+t}\| < \epsilon.$$

thus,

$$\| x_{n+1} + \cdots + x_{n+t} \| < \epsilon,$$

or

$$\| s_{n+t} - s_n \| < \epsilon,$$

where $s_n = \sum_{k=1}^{n} x_k$. Therefore, $\{s_n\}$ is a Cauchy sequence in X, and $\lim s_n$ exists since X is complete. Also,

$$\| x_1 + \cdots + x_n \| \leqslant \| x_1 \| + \cdots + \| x_n \|,$$

so

$$\| s_n \| \leqslant \sum_{n=1}^{\infty} \| x_n \|,$$

for any n. Hence,

$$\left\| \sum_{n=1}^{\infty} x_n \right\| \leqslant \sum_{n=1}^{\infty} \| x_n \|,$$

and this completes the proof.

It is readily seen that one can manipulate with absolutely convergent series in a Banach space just as one does in the case case of absolutely convergent series of real or complex numbers.

2. Linear Functionals

We shall assume throughout this section that X is a normed linear space over k, where $k = C$ or R, with the customary absolute value, i.e., X is a complex or real linear space. Let $f : X \to k$ be a linear functional, i.e., $f(\alpha x + \beta y) = \alpha f(x) + \beta f(y)$ for all x, $y \in X$ and all α, $\beta \in k$. We shall also consider subsequently linear functionals which are not defined on all of X but only on some domain $D_f \subset X$, where D_f is a subspace of X.

We show first of all that if f is a linear functional defined on X and if f is continuous at just a single point of X, it automatically follows that f is continuous on all of X.

Theorem 2.1. If the linear functional f is continuous at some point x of the normed linear space X, then f is continuous everywhere on X.

Proof. Since f is continuous at x, we have that for every sequence $x_n \to x$, $f(x_n) \to f(x)$. Let y be an arbitrary point of X and let $\{y_n\}$ be an arbitrary sequence in X such that $y_n \to y$. Then

$$f(y_n) = f(y_n - y + x + y - x) = f(y_n - y + x) + f(y) - f(x).$$

However, $y_n - y + x \to x$, and, by the continuity of f at x, it follows that

$$f(y_n - y + x) \to f(x).$$

Thus,

$$f(y_n) \to f(x) + f(y) - f(x) = f(y),$$

which completes the proof.

We observe that actually all that was needed for the proof was the fact that f was additive, i.e., $f(x + y) = f(x) + f(y)$ for all $x, y \in X$. However, we shall not make use of this fact since we shall be concerned throughout this section with linear functionals.

Definition 2.1. A linear functional f is said to be *bounded* if there exists a real number $a \geqslant 0$ such that $|f(x)| \leqslant a \|x\|$ for all $x \in X$.

Similarly one defines a bounded linear functional f defined on a subspace D_f of X. For a linear functional, the concepts of boundedness and continuity are equivalent, namely:

Theorem 2.2. If f is a linear functional defined in X, then f is bounded if and only if it is continuous.

Proof. Assume first that f is continuous. If f were not bounded, then, for an arbitrary positive integer n, there exists an element $x_n \in X$ such that

$$|f(x_n)| > n \|x_n\|.$$

Let $y_n = x_n/n\|x_n\|$. Clearly, $\|y_n\| = 1/n$, and, therefore, $y_n \to 0$. But

$$|f(y_n)| = \left| f\left(\frac{x_n}{n\|x_n\|}\right)\right| = \frac{1}{n\|x_n\|}|f(x_n)| > 1,$$

which contradicts the assumption that f is continuous.

Conversely, suppose that f is bounded and let a be a real number such that $|f(x)| \leqslant a\|x\|$ for all $x \in X$. Then, if $\{x_n\}$ is an arbitrary sequence of elements of X such that $x_n \to 0$,

$$|f(x_n)| \leqslant a\|x_n\| \to 0.$$

Thus, f is continuous at $x = 0$, and, by the preceding theorem, f is continuous everywhere.

We now introduce the notion of the norm of a bounded linear functional. We observe that since f is bounded the set of all $|f(x)|/\|x\|$ where $x \neq 0$ is a bounded set of real numbers, and, therefore has a least upper bound.

Definition 2.2. Let f be a bounded linear functional on X, the *norm* of f, denoted by $\|f\|$, is defined as follows:

$$\|f\| = \sup_{x \neq 0} \frac{|f(x)|}{\|x\|}.$$

It follows immediately that $\|f\|$ is precisely the infinum of the set of all real numbers a which satisfy Definition 2.1. It is also clear that

$$|f(x)| \leqslant \|f\|\|x\| \qquad \text{for all } x \in X,$$

and, if ϵ is an arbitrary positive real number, there exist an $x' \in X$ such that

$$|f(x')| > (\|f\| - \epsilon)\|x'\|.$$

The norm of f can also be expressed as follows:

$$\|f\| = \sup_{\|x\| \leqslant 1} |f(x)|. \tag{2.1}$$

This is readily seen to be true, for if $\|x\| \leqslant 1$, then

$$|f(x)| \leqslant \|f\| \|x\| \leqslant \|f\|,$$

so $\sup_{\|x\| \leqslant 1} |f(x)| \leqslant \|f\|$. If $\epsilon > 0$, then there exists an $x' \in X$ such that

$$|f(x')| > (\|f\| - \epsilon) \|x'\|.$$

Let $x_1 = x'/\|x'\|$. Then $\|x_1\| = 1$, and

$$|f(x_1)| = \frac{1}{\|x'\|} |f(x')| > \frac{1}{\|x'\|} (\|f\| - \epsilon) \|x'\| = \|f\| - \epsilon;$$

therefore,

$$\sup_{\|x\| \leqslant 1} |f(x)| \geqslant f(x_1)| > \|f\| - \epsilon.$$

Since ϵ is an arbitrary positive real number, we have $\sup_{\|x\| \leqslant 1} |f(x)| \geqslant \|f\|$, and this completes the proof of (2.1). Actually, the proof shows a little more, namely, that

$$\|f\| = \sup_{\|x\|=1} |f(x)|.$$

We note that in the finite-dimensional case, every linear functional on X is bounded. For let f be a linear functional defined on X and let $x_1, x_2, ..., x_n$ be a basis of X. Then, if $x \in X$, $x = \sum_{i=1}^{n} \alpha_i x_i$, uniquely. Then

$$f(x) = \sum_{i=1}^{n} \alpha_i f(x_i),$$

so

$$|f(x)| \leqslant \sum_{i=1}^{n} |\alpha_i| |f(x_i)|$$

$$\leqslant \|x\|_0 \sum_{i=1}^{n} |f(x_i)|$$

$$= a \|x\|_0 ,$$

where $a = \sum_{i=1}^{n} |f(x_i)|$, and $\|\ \|_0$ is the special norm used in the proof of Theorem 1.2 of the preceding section. Thus, we have shown that f is bounded in the norm $\| \ \|_0$, and, since any two norms on X are equivalent by Theorem 1.2, we have established the contention.

This is certainly not the case for X infinite dimensional. For example, consider the subspace M of $C\ [0, 1]$ consisting of differentiable functions, and define $f : M \to C$, by $f(x) = x'(1)$. f is certainly linear, but for $x_n(t) = t^n$,

$$f(x_n) = x_n'(1) = n,$$

from which it follows that f is not bounded.

The next notion we shall introduce is that of a sublinear functional.

Definition 2.3. Let X be just a linear space over C or R. The real-valued function, $p : X \to R$, is called a *sublinear functional* if

(1) $p(x + y) \leqslant p(x) + p(y)$ for all $x, y \in X$;

(2) $p(\alpha x) = \alpha p(x)$ for all real $\alpha \geqslant 0$ and all $x \in X$.

If, in addition, $p(x) \geqslant 0$ for all $x \in X$, then p is called a *convex functional*.

Our aim now is to establish the important Hahn-Banach theorem. In order to do this, we shall establish first the following lemma from which the theorem will follow readily.

Lemma. Let M be a subspace of the real linear space X. Suppose that p is a sublinear functional defined on N, which is the subspace spanned by M and some $x_0 \notin M$; also, assume that f is a linear functional defined on M such that

$$f(x) \leqslant p(x) \qquad \text{for all } x \in M.$$

Then f can be extended to a linear functional g defined on N such that

$$g(x) \leqslant p(x) \qquad \text{for all } x \in N.$$

Proof. We first note that any element $y \in N$ can be written uniquely in the form

$$y = x + \alpha x_0 \tag{2.2}$$

where $x \in M$ and $\alpha \in R$, for if

$$x_1 + \alpha_1 x_0 = x_2 + \alpha_2 x_0$$

$x_1, x_2 \in M$, $\alpha_1, \alpha_2 \in R$, then

$$x_1 - x_2 = (\alpha_2 - \alpha_1) x_0,$$

which implies, if $\alpha_2 - \alpha_1 \neq 0$, that $x_0 \in M$, a contradiction. Hence, $\alpha_1 = \alpha_2$, and then $x_1 = x_2$, so the representation (2.2) is unique.

Next, let x_1, x_2 be arbitrary elements of M; then

$$f(x_1) - f(x_2) = f(x_1 - x_2) \leqslant p(x_1 - x_2) = p((x_1 + x_0) - (x_2 + x_0))$$
$$\leqslant p(x_1 + x_0) + p(-x_2 - x_0).$$

Hence,

$$-p(-x_2 - x_0) - f(x_2) \leqslant p(x_1 + x_0) - f(x_1). \tag{2.3}$$

Since x_1 and x_2 are arbitrary elements of M, it follows from (2.3) that

$$a = \sup_{x \in M} (-p(-x - x_0) - f(x))$$

and

$$b = \inf_{x \in M} (p(x + x_0) - f(x))$$

are finite. Moreover, $a \leqslant b$. We now choose c to be any real number such that $a \leqslant c \leqslant b$. Then for arbitrary $y = x + \alpha x_0 \in N$, we define

$$g(y) = f(x) + \alpha c. \tag{2.4}$$

g is clearly a linear functional defined on N, since for $y_1 = x_1 + \alpha_1 x_0$, and $y_2 = x_2 + \alpha_2 x_0$ in N,

$$g(y_1 + y_2) = f(x_1 + x_2) + c(\alpha_1 + \alpha_2)$$
$$= f(x_1) + c\alpha_1 + f(x_2) + c\alpha_2$$
$$= g(y_1) + g(y_2).$$

Similarly, $g(\beta y) = \beta g(y)$ for $\beta \in R$. Also, g extends f since, for $x \in M$, $\alpha = 0$ in (2.4), and $g(x) = f(x)$. Thus, to complete the proof of the lemma, we must show that $g(y) \leqslant p(y)$ for all $y \in N$, i.e., we must show that

$$f(x) + \alpha c \leqslant p(x + \alpha x_0) \qquad (2.5)$$

for all $x \in M$ and all $\alpha \in R$. Equation (2.5) is true for $\alpha = 0$ by the hypothesis, so we may assume that $\alpha \neq 0$. Now, since c was chosen between a and b, we have

$$-p(-x - x_0) - f(x) \leqslant c \leqslant p(x + x_0) - f(x) \qquad (2.6)$$

for all $x \in M$. We assume first that $\alpha > 0$ and replace x by $(1/\alpha)\, x$ on the right-hand side of (2.6). Then

$$c \leqslant p\left(\frac{x}{\alpha} + x_0\right) - f\left(\frac{x}{\alpha}\right),$$

and, since $\alpha > 0$, we have

$$\alpha f\left(\frac{x}{\alpha}\right) + \alpha c \leqslant \alpha p\left(\frac{x}{\alpha} + x_0\right),$$

or

$$f(x) + \alpha c \leqslant p(x + \alpha x_0)$$

since f is linear and p is sublinear. Thus (2.5) is true for $\alpha > 0$. Now suppose that $\alpha < 0$. We replace x by $(1/\alpha)\, x$ on the left-hand side of (2.6). This yields

$$-p\left(-\frac{x}{\alpha} - x_0\right) - f\left(\frac{x}{\alpha}\right) \leqslant c.$$

If we multiply by α, we reverse the inequality and get

$$-\alpha p \left(-\frac{x}{\alpha} - x_0 \right) - \alpha f \left(\frac{x}{\alpha} \right) \geqslant \alpha c.$$

or

$$(-\alpha) \, p \left(-\frac{x}{\alpha} - x_0 \right) \geqslant \alpha c + \alpha f \left(\frac{x}{\alpha} \right).$$

Again, by the linearity of f and the sublinearity of p, we have

$$p(x + \alpha x_0) \geqslant \alpha c + f(x),$$

which shows that (2.5) is true also for $\alpha < 0$ and completes the proof of the lemma.

Theorem 2.3.   Let p be a sublinear functional defined on the real linear space X and let M be a subspace of X. Suppose that f is a linear functional defined on M such that $f(x) \leqslant p(x)$ for all $x \in M$. Then f can be extended to a linear functional F defined on all of X such that $F(x) \leqslant p(x)$ for all $x \in X$.

Proof.   We denote by $S = \{g_\alpha\}$ the set of all linear functionals which extend f and which are such that $g_\alpha(x) \leqslant p(x)$ for all $x \in D_\alpha$, the domain of g_α. For $g_\alpha , g_\beta \in S$, we define $g_\beta > g_\alpha$ if g_β is an extension of g_α. This clearly gives a partial ordering in S. If $\{g_\nu\}$ is a totally ordered subset of S, then the domains D_ν of the g_ν are totally ordered by set inclusion. We define h on $\bigcup_\nu D_\nu$ by $h(x) = g_\nu(x)$ for $x \in D_\nu$. h is well defined since the set $\{g_\nu\}$ is totally ordered; also h is clearly linear and belongs to S. Finally, $h >$ any g_ν in the totally ordered subset. Thus, S is inductively ordered, and, therefore, by Zorn's lemma S has a maximal element F. F must be defined on all of X for otherwise, using the lemma, there exists a proper extension of F, but this would contradict the maximality of F. Thus, F is defined in all of X, and since $F \in S$, F extends f, and $F(x) \leqslant p(x)$ for all $x \in X$. This completes the proof.

We want next to consider the situation for complex linear spaces. For this purpose, we introduce the notion of a symmetric convex functional.

Definition 2.4. A convex functional p defined on the real or complex linear space X is called *symmetric* if $p(\alpha x) = |\alpha| p(x)$ for all $x \in X$ and for all α belonging to R or C.

Now we can state and prove the analog of Theorem 2.3 for complex linear spaces.

Theorem 2.4. Let p be a symmetric convex functional defined on the complex linear space X and let M be a subspace of X. Suppose that f is a linear functional defined on M such that

$$|f(x)| \leqslant p(x) \qquad \text{for all } x \in M.$$

Then f can be extended to a linear functional F defined on X such that

$$|F(x)| \leqslant p(x) \qquad \text{for all } x \in X.$$

Proof. Since X is a complex space, it can also be viewed as a real space. The linear functional f on M can be decomposed into a real and imaginary part, namely,

$$f(x) = g(x) + ih(x), \qquad x \in M, \tag{2.7}$$

where g and h are real-valued functions. Moreover, g and h are real linear functionals on M, i.e.,

$$g(\alpha x + \beta y) = \alpha g(x) + \beta g(y), \quad \text{and} \quad h(\alpha x + \beta y) = \alpha h(x) + \beta h(y)$$

for all $x, y \in M$ and all $\alpha, \beta \in R$. The proof of this follows readily from (2.7) and from the fact that $\alpha, \beta \in R$.

Next, we have, by hypothesis, that

$$g(x) \leqslant |f(x)| \leqslant p(x) \qquad \text{for all } x \in M.$$

Thus, the real-valued real linear functional g defined on M, which can be viewed as a real subspace, satisfies the conditions of Theorem 2.3. Hence, there exists a real-valued real linear functional G defined on all of X such that

$$G(x) \leqslant p(x) \qquad \text{for all } x \in X. \tag{2.8}$$

We define

$$F(x) = G(x) - iG(ix). \qquad (2.9)$$

Observe first that, for $x \in M$,

$$if(x) = i(g(x) + ih(x)) = -h(x) + ig(x),$$

but $if(x) = f(ix)$ since f is given as linear on M. Now,

$$f(ix) = g(ix) + ih(ix).$$

Therefore,

$$g(ix) = -h(x), \qquad x \in M. \qquad (2.10)$$

Let $x \in M$, then

$$\begin{aligned}
F(x) &= G(x) - iG(ix) \\
&= g(x) - ig(ix) \\
&= g(x) - i(-h(x)) \\
&= g(x) + ih(x) \\
&= f(x),
\end{aligned}$$

where we have made use of (2.7), (2.10), and the fact that G extends g. Thus, F extends f. F is certainly real-linear since G is, but it is even complex linear since.

$$\begin{aligned}
F(ix) &= G(ix) - iG(-x) \\
&= G(ix) + iG(x);
\end{aligned}$$

while

$$\begin{aligned}
iF(x) &= i(G(x) - iG(ix)) \\
&= iG(x) + G(ix).
\end{aligned}$$

Thus, F is a linear functional on the complex linear space X, and F extends f. Hence, to complete the proof, we must just show that F satisfies the desired inequality. This is certainly the case if $F(x) = 0$. If $F(x) \neq 0$, let $F(x) = re^{i\theta}$.

$$F(e^{-i\theta}x) = e^{-i\theta}F(x) = e^{-i\theta}(re^{i\theta}) = r.$$

Hence,

$$|F(x)| = r = F(e^{-i\theta}x) = G(e^{-i\theta}x)$$

since $F(e^{-i\theta}x)$ is real. But

$$G(e^{-i\theta}x) \leqslant p(e^{-i\theta}x)$$

by (2.8). Thus,

$$|F(x)| \leqslant p(e^{-i\theta}x) = p(x)$$

since p is symmetric. This completes the proof.

Now we continue to consider the situation where X is a normed linear space over C. Let f be a bounded linear functional defined on a subspace M. We shall choose a special symmetric convex functional on X and apply the preceding theorem to this case; namely, define

$$p(x) = \|f\| \|x\| \qquad \text{for all } x \in X,$$

where $\|f\|$ is the norm of f defined on M. Then, by definition of the norm of f,

$$|f(x)| \leqslant \|f\| \|x\| = p(x) \qquad \text{for all } x \in M;$$

also,

$$p(x + y) = \|f\| \|x + y\| \leqslant \|f\| (\|x\| + \|y\|)$$
$$= p(x) + p(y).$$
$$p(\alpha x) = \|f\| \|\alpha x\| = |\alpha| \|f\| \|x\| = |\alpha| p(x).$$

Thus, p is a symmetric convex functional, and $|f(x)| \leqslant p(x)$ for all $x \in M$. Therefore, by Theorem 2.4, there exists a linear functional F defined on X which extends f, and is such that

$$|F(x)| \leqslant p(x) = \|f\| \|x\| \qquad \text{for all } x \in X.$$

This implies that $\|F\| \leqslant \|f\|$, but it is clear that $\|F\| \geqslant \|f\|$ since F extends f. Thus, we have shown the following:

Theorem 2.5. If X is a normed complex linear space, and if M is a subspace of X, then, if f is a bounded linear functional defined on M, f can be extended to a linear functional defined on all of X with the same norm as f.

Of course, the theorem is also true for real normed linear spaces.

As an immediate consequence of the theorem, we have:

Corollary. If X is a normed linear space over C or R, and if $x \in X$, and $x \neq 0$, then there exists a bounded linear functional, F, defined on X such that $\| F \| = 1$, and $F(x) = \| x \|$.

Proof. Let M be the subspace of X spanned by x. Then, for $y \in M$, $y = \alpha x$, and we define

$$f(y) = \alpha \| x \|.$$

f is clearly linear on M, and f is bounded with norm 1 since

$$| f(y) | = | \alpha | \| x \| = \| y \|$$

for all $y \in M$. Therefore, by Theorem 2.5, there exists a bounded linear functional F defined on X which extends f, and such that $\| F \| = \| f \| = 1$. Since F extends f,

$$F(x) = f(x) = \| x \|,$$

and the proof has been completed.

We see from the corollary that if $f(x) = 0$ for every bounded linear functional f defined on X, we must have $x = 0$.

3. Banach Algebras

We shall now give a brief introduction to the notion of Banach algebras and we shall derive several consequences from the definition. Our main aim in this section is to prove the important theorem of Gel'fand on commutative Banach algebras which are fields. This theorem will be applied in the next chapter to the extension problem for valuations, but it is also the starting point of the Gel'fand theory of commutative Banach algebras. We refer the reader to the Bibliography at the end of the book for further details.

Definition 3.1. A *normed algebra* over C is a set X which satisfies the following conditions:

(a) X is a normed linear space over C;

(b) X is a ring;

(c) $\alpha(xy) = (\alpha x)y = x(\alpha y)$ for all $x, y \in X$, $\alpha \in C$;

(d) $\|xy\| \leqslant \|x\|\|y\|$.

We shall assume throughout that all our normed algebras are *commutative*, i.e., $xy = yx$ for all $x, y \in X$, and we shall also assume that X contains an *identity* element e. Hence, $ex = xe = x$ for all $x \in X$.

Theorem 3.1. Let X be a normed algebra. The operation of ring multiplication in X is continuous.

Proof. Let $x, y, x_0, y_0 \in X$. Then

$$\|xy - x_0 y_0\| = \|(x - x_0)(y - y_0) + y_0(x - x_0) + x_0(y - y_0)\|$$
$$\leqslant \|x - x_0\|\|y - y_0\| + \|y_0\|\|x - x_0\| + \|x_0\|\|y - y_0\|,$$

and the theorem follows immediately from this inequality.

If the normed algebra X is complete with respect to the norm, i.e., if X is also a Banach space, then X is called a *Banach algebra*.

Theorem 3.2. Let X be a Banach algebra.

(a) If $x \in X$, and if $\|e - x\| < 1$, then x is a unit of X.

(b) If $|\lambda| > \|x\|$, where $\lambda \in C$, $x \in X$, then $(x - \lambda e)$ is a unit of X.

Proof. We consider the series

$$e + (e - x) + (e - x)^2 + \cdots. \tag{3.1}$$

Since $\|(e - x)^n\| \leqslant \|e - x\|^n$, and since $\|e - x\| < 1$, by hypothesis, the series (3.1) converges absolutely, and, therefore, converges by Theorem 1.4 of this chapter. Multiply the series (3.1) by $x = e - (e - x)$. Then we have

$$e + (e - x) + (e - x)^2 + \cdots - (e - x) - (e - x)^2 - \cdots = e$$

Thus, the convergent series (3.1) represents the inverse element of x, and statement (a) has been established.

To prove (b), we write

$$(x - \lambda e) = \lambda \left(\frac{1}{\lambda} x - e \right).$$

Since $\lambda \neq 0$, we must just show that $((1/\lambda) x - e)$ is invertible. However,

$$\left\| \frac{1}{\lambda} x \right\| = \frac{1}{|\lambda|} \| x \| < 1$$

Therefore, by part (a), $((1/\lambda) x - e)$ is invertible, and the proof is complete.

Let us denote by A the set of all elements of X which are units. Then $e \in A$, and, by part (a) of Theorem 3.2, the neighborhood of e:

$$N(e) = \{ x \in X \mid \| e - x \| < 1 \}$$

is contained in A. Let $x \in A$, then x^{-1} exists, and $xx^{-1} = e$. By Theorem 3.1, the ring multiplication is continuous; hence, there exists a neighborhood of x, $N(x)$, such that

$$N(x) \, x^{-1} \subset N(e).$$

Thus, for all $y \in N(x)$, $yx^{-1} \in N(e) \subset A$. Hence, yx^{-1} is invertible, i.e., there exists a $z \in X$ such that $yx^{-1}z = e$, but then y is also invertible. Therefore, $N(x) \subset A$, which implies that A is an open set.

Theorem 3.3. The map: $A \to A$ given by $x \to x^{-1}$ (where A is, as above, the set of all elements of the Banach algebra X which are units) is continuous.

Proof. Let $\{x_n\}$ be an arbitrary sequence of elements of A such that $x_n \to x$, where $x \in A$. Then $x^{-1}x_n \to e$. Now, $(x^{-1}x_n)^{-1}$ can be expressed by the geometric series

$$(x^{-1}x_n)^{-1} = e + (e - x^{-1}x_n) + (e - x^{-1}x_n)^2 + \cdots.$$

Thus

$$e - x_n^{-1}x = -(e - x^{-1}x_n) - (e - x^{-1}x_n)^2 - \cdots,$$

and recalling Theorem 1.4 of this chapter, we have

$$\| e - x_n^{-1}x \| \leqslant \sum_{k=1}^{\infty} \| (e - x^{-1}x_n)^k \|$$

$$= \sum_{k=1}^{\infty} \| x^{-k}(x - x_n)^k \|$$

$$\leqslant \sum_{k=1}^{\infty} \| x^{-1} \|^k \| x - x_n \|^k.$$

This clearly implies that $x_n^{-1}x \to e$, or $x_n^{-1} \to x^{-1}$, which proves the theorem.

Let $x \in X$, and let $\lambda \in C$. λ is called a *regular point* of x if $(x - \lambda e)$ is a unit of X. The set, $\sigma(x)$, of all nonregular points of x is called the *spectrum* of x. Hence, $\lambda \in \sigma(x)$ implies that $(x - \lambda e)$ is not invertible. If λ is a regular point of x, then $(x - \lambda e) \in A$, and, since the inverse operation is continuous on the open set A, we see that there exists a neighborhood of $(x - \lambda e)$ such that all elements y in this neighborhood have inverses. However, by the continuity of the function $x - \alpha e$ as a function of $\alpha \in C$, there exists a neighborhood of λ, which maps into the neighborhood or $x - \lambda e$. This shows that the set of regular points of x is an open set in C. Therefore, $\sigma(x)$, the spectrum of x, is a closed set in C. However, if $| \lambda | > \| x \|$, then $(x - \lambda e) \in A$ by the second part of Theorem 3.2. Thus, $\sigma(x)$ is also bounded and is, consequently, a compact subset of C. We wish to establish that $\sigma(x)$ is also non-empty. In order to achieve this, we shall introduce one more concept in Banach algebras. We could actually have defined this notion earlier for normed linear spaces, but we only need it for the special situation at hand.

Definition 3.2. Let G be a domain in the complex plane and let x be a vector-valued function: $x : G \to X$, where X is a

Banach algebra, i.e., for $\lambda \in G$, $x(\lambda) \in X$. x is defined to be *analytic* in G if

$$x'(\lambda_0) = \lim_{\lambda \to \lambda_0} \frac{x(\lambda) - x(\lambda_0)}{\lambda - \lambda_0}$$

exists for all $\lambda_0 \in G$.

Let f be an arbitrary bounded linear functional on X, and suppose that $x(\lambda)$ is analytic in G. $f(x(\lambda))$ is an ordinary complex-valued function on G, and it is analytic on G in the usual sense, for, since f is bounded, f is continuous; whence,

$$\lim_{\lambda \to \lambda_0} \frac{f(x(\lambda)) - f(x(\lambda_0))}{\lambda - \lambda_0} = f(x'(\lambda_0))$$

exists also for all $\lambda_0 \in G$.

Now, we shall establish Liouville's theorem for analytic vector-valued functions.

Theorem 3.4. If $x(\lambda)$ is analytic in the entire complex plane and bounded, then it is a constant.

Proof. Let f be an arbitrary bounded linear functional on X. Then, as noted above, $f(x(\lambda))$ is analytic in the entire complex plane also. Moreover,

$$|f(x(\lambda))| \leqslant \|f\| \, \|x(\lambda)\|,$$

and, since $\|x(\lambda)\|$ is bounded, $|f(x(\lambda))|$ is bounded. Thus, by the ordinary Liouville theorem, $f(x(\lambda))$ is a constant. Hence, for arbitrary complex numbers α, β,

$$f(x(\alpha)) = f(x(\beta)),$$

or

$$f(x(\alpha) - x(\beta)) = 0,$$

where f was any bounded linear functional. Thus, by the corollary of Theorem 2.5 of this chapter, we must have $x(\alpha) - x(\beta) = 0$, for any α, $\beta \in C$. Therefore $x(\lambda)$ is a constant, which is what we wanted to prove.

Now, let x be a fixed element of X. We consider the vector-valued function

$$x(\lambda) = (x - \lambda e)^{-1}.$$

Suppose that λ_1 and λ_2 are regular points of x. Then

$$\begin{aligned}
x(\lambda_1)^{-1} x(\lambda_2) &= (x - \lambda_1 e) \, x(\lambda_2) \\
&= [(x - \lambda_2 e) + (\lambda_2 - \lambda_1) \, e] \, x(\lambda_2) \\
&= e + (\lambda_2 - \lambda_1) \, x(\lambda_2).
\end{aligned}$$

Hence, $x(\lambda_2) = x(\lambda_1) + (\lambda_2 - \lambda_1) \, x(\lambda_1) \, x(\lambda_2)$, or

$$x(\lambda_2) - x(\lambda_1) = (\lambda_2 - \lambda_1) \, x(\lambda_1) \, x(\lambda_2). \tag{3.2}$$

We have also seen that the regular points of x form an open set in C, and we can now, with the aid of (3.2), prove the following:

Theorem 3.5. The vector-valued function $x(\lambda) = (x - \lambda e)^{-1}$ is analytic in the set of all regular points of x.

Proof. For arbitrary distinct λ, λ_0 in the set of regular points of x, we have, using (3.2), that

$$\frac{x(\lambda) - x(\lambda_0)}{\lambda - \lambda_0} = x(\lambda) \, x(\lambda_0).$$

As $\lambda \to \lambda_0$, $x(\lambda) \to x(\lambda_0)$ by Theorem 3.3 and by the continuity of $x - \lambda e$ as a function of λ. Thus,

$$\lim_{\lambda \to \lambda_0} \frac{x(\lambda) - x(\lambda_0)}{\lambda - \lambda_0} = x(\lambda_0)^2,$$

which completes the proof. We can now prove that, for $x \in X$, $\sigma(x)$ is not empty.

Theorem 3.6. If X is a Banach algebra and if $x \in X$, then $\sigma(x)$, the spectrum of x, is a nonempty set.

Proof. Suppose $\sigma(x)$ is empty. Then the set of regular points of x coincides with the entire complex plane, and $(x - \lambda e)^{-1}$

exists for all $\lambda \in C$. This function is, therefore, analytic in the entire plane by Theorem 3.5. Furthermore, for $\lambda \neq 0$, $e - \lambda^{-1}x \to e$ as $|\lambda| \to \infty$; therefore, by Theorem 3.3,

$$(e - \lambda^{-1}x)^{-1} \to e.$$

Hence,

$$\| (x - \lambda e)^{-1} \| = | \lambda^{-1} | \, \| (e - \lambda^{-1}x)^{-1} \| \to 0 \qquad (3.3)$$

as $|\lambda| \to \infty$. Thus the function $x(\lambda) = (x - \lambda e)^{-1}$ is analytic in the entire complex plane and is bounded. Using Theorem 3.4, we get that $(x - \lambda e)^{-1}$ is a constant, which must be 0 by (3.3); i.e., $(x - \lambda e)^{-1} = 0$, which is absurd since

$$(x - \lambda e) \, (x - \lambda e)^{-1} = e.$$

It is now a simple matter, on the basis of Theorem 3.6, to establish the Gel'fand theorem.

Theorem 3.7. If X is a Banach algebra (commutative, as usual) which is a field, then X is isomorphic to the field of complex numbers.

Proof. Let $x \in X$, $\sigma(x) \neq \phi$ by Theorem 3.6. Let $\lambda \in \sigma(x)$, then $(x - \lambda e)$ is not invertible. However, X is a field so every nonzero element is a unit. Thus, we must have $x - \lambda e = 0$, or $x = \lambda e$. In other words, every element $x \in X$ is of the form λe for some $\lambda \in C$. The mapping, $X \to C$, given by $\lambda e \to \lambda$ now yields the desired isomorphism.

This completes our short excursion through normed spaces and Banach algebras. For the most part, we have just proved things which will be needed for the discussion in the next chapter. However, we again hope that the trip was worthwhile for the reader in the sense that he will be motivated to discover more of the properties and applications of the structures, which we have considered all too briefly in this chapter. References are, for example, Naimark [15], Lorch [14], Hille and Phillips [9].

CHAPTER V

Extensions of Valuations

1. The Extension Problem

In this chapter, we shall be concerned for the most part with the problem of extending a rank one valuation on a given field to a finite extension field. We shall see that it is always possible to do this; however, we shall have to handle the archimedian and non-archimedian cases separately. If the given field is complete with respect to the valuation, it will be seen that the extension is unique, and an explicit formula for it will be obtained. We shall next consider the number of different extensions which are possible when the given field is not complete. In the course of the development, a number of concepts will be introduced and some results will be obtained which are important beyond just the extension problem.

We shall begin the discussion with the case of a given field k with a rank one valuation $|\ |$ such that k is complete with respect to $|\ |$. K will denote a finite extension field of degree n of k. We shall show that, if the valuation can be extended to K, the extension is unique.

Since K is a finite extension field of degree n of k, K can be viewed as a finite-dimensional vector space of dimension n over k. Let $x_1, x_2, ..., x_n$ denote a basis of K over k. We denote the extension of $|\ |$ on the complete field k to K again by $|\ |$. $|\ |$, being a valuation on K, makes K a normed linear space over k according to Definition 1.1 of Chapter IV. If $x \in K$, we can write

$$x = \alpha_1 x_1 + \alpha_2 x_2 + \cdots + \alpha_n x_n \tag{1.1}$$

in a unique way where the $\alpha_i \in k$. If we set

$$\| x \|_0 = \max_i |\alpha_i|,$$

then this is also a norm on K, as we noted in the proof of Theorem 1.2 of the previous chapter. However, by this same theorem,

$\| \ \|_0$ and $| \ |$ must be equivalent. Also, K is complete with respect to either norm by IV, Theorem 1.3.

Suppose that $| x | < 1$, then $| x |^r \to 0$, so $| x^r | \to 0$, which implies, by the equivalency, that $\| x^r \|_0 \to 0$. But this means, writing

$$x^r = \alpha_{r1}x_1 + \alpha_{r2}x_2 + \cdots + \alpha_{rn}x_n \ ,$$

that

$$\lim_{r \to \infty} | \alpha_{ri} | = 0, \qquad i = 1, 2, ..., n. \tag{1.2}$$

Now, the norm of x, $N_{K|_k}(x) = N(x)$, for x given by (1.1) is a homogeneous polynomial of degree n in the α_i with coefficients in k. Thus, we must have

$$\lim_{r \to \infty} | N(x^r) | = 0, \tag{1.3}$$

for $N(x^r)$ is a homogeneous polynomial of degree n in the α_{ri} with fixed coefficients in k for all r, and then use (1.2). By the multiplicative property of the norm and by the multiplicative property of the valuation, (1.3) can be written as

$$\lim_{r \to \infty} | N(x) |^r = 0, \tag{1.4}$$

which implies that $| N(x) | < 1$. We have, therefore, shown that if $| x | < 1$, then $| N(x) | < 1$.

If $| x | > 1$, then $| 1/x | < 1$; whence $| N(1/x) | < 1$, but $N(1/x) = N(x)^{-1}$. Thus, $| N(x) |^{-1} < 1$, and $| N(x) | > 1$. Hence, if $| N(x) | = 1$, then we must have $| x | = 1$.

Finally, for $x \in K$, and $x \neq 0$, let $y = N(x)/x^n \in K$. Then

$$N(y) = \frac{N(N(x))}{N(x^n)} = \frac{N(x)^n}{N(x)^n} = 1,$$

which implies, by what we just noted, that $| y | = 1$, i.e.,

$$\left| \frac{N(x)}{x^n} \right| = 1,$$

or

$$| N(x) | = | x |^n,$$

and

$$| x | = \sqrt[n]{| N(x) |}, \tag{1.5}$$

for all $x \neq 0$ in K, but (1.5) is clearly true for $x = 0$. Thus, (1.5) holds for all $x \in K$ and shows:

Theorem 1.1. If a rank one valuation of the complete field k has an extension as a rank one valuation to a finite extension field K of degree n over k, the extension is unique and is given by (1.5).

In particular, we note that the trivial valuation of a field k does not have any nontrivial extensions to finite extension fields. This is certainly not the case for infinite extension fields as we observed in the example of the rational function fields of I, 2.

Now, we turn attention to the extension problem. Here, as noted earlier, we shall have to consider separately the archimedian and non-archimedian cases. We consider first the non-archimedian case in general, i.e., we let $| \ |_k$ be an arbitrary non-archimedian valuation of a field k, not necessarily complete, with associated place, φ, and associated valuation ring V_k, with units U_k and non-units P_k. Recalling the discussion in III, 2, we have $| k^* |_k \simeq k^*/U_k$, and there is an equivalent valuation with ordered group k^*/U_k, such that $| aU_k | < 1$ if and only if $a \in P_k^* = P_k - \{0\}$.

Next, let K be an arbitrary, not necessarily finite, extension field of k. We want to show that $| \ |_k$ can be extended to K. As noted in III, 4, we may assume

$$\varphi : \quad k \to F \cup \{\infty\},$$

where F is an algebraically closed field. If we consider φ restricted to V_k, then

$$\varphi |_{V_k} : \quad V_k \to F,$$

where F is algebraically closed, and where $\varphi |_{V_k}$ is nontrivial. We note here that we may assume throughout that $| \ |_k$ is not trivial since the trivial valuation on k can always be extended to a trivial valuation on K. Now, by the extension theorem of III, 4, $\varphi \mid_{V_k}$ can be extended to a place ψ of K. We designate the associated valuation by $\mid \mid_K$, the associated valuation ring by V_K, the units and non-units by U_K and P_K, respectively.

If $a \in V_k$, then $\varphi(a) \in F$; whence, $\psi(a) \in F$ since ψ is an extension of $\varphi \mid_{V_k}$. But $\psi(a) \in F$ implies that $a \in V_K$. Thus $V_k \subset V_K$. Now, let $a \in k$ and $a \notin V_k$, then $\varphi(a) = \infty$, so $\varphi(1/a) = 0$; therefore, $\psi(1/a) = 0$, and $\psi(a) = \infty$, i.e., $a \notin V_K$. Thus,

$$V_k = k \cap V_K, \qquad (1.6)$$

and $\psi \mid_k = \varphi$.

$\mid \mid_K$ restricted to k gives clearly a valuation on k, and for $a \in k$, $\mid a \mid_K \leqslant 1$ means that $a \in k \cap V_K = V_k$. Hence, $\mid \mid_K$ restricted to k is a valuation of k equivalent to $\mid \mid_k$, the given one. Moreover, from (1.6) and from III, (1.2), we have

$$K - V_k = K - k \cup K - V_K,$$

so

$$k - V_k = k \cap (K - V_K),$$

i.e.,

$$(P_k - \{0\})^{-1} = k \cap (P_K - \{0\})^{-1}.$$

Therefore,

$$P_k = k \cap P_K,$$

and, consequently,

$$U_k = k \cap U_K.$$

We can now embed k^*/U_k in K^*/U_K in an order isomorphic fashion by mapping:

$$aU_k \to aU_K.$$

The mapping is well defined for, if $b \in U_k$, then $abU_k \to abU_K = aU_K$. It is clearly a homomorphism, and, if $aU_K = U_K$, then $a \in U_K \cap k = U_k$. Thus, it is isomorphism. Finally, it is order preserving for $aU_k < bU_k$ implies that $ab^{-1} \in P_k = P_K \cap k$, so $aU_K < bU_K$. Also, $|k^*|_k$ is order isomorphic to k^*/U_k, and $|K^*|_K$ is order isomorphic to K^*/U_K.

Similarly, the mapping

$$a + P_k \to a + P_K$$

is an isomorphism of V_k/P_k into V_K/P_K.

Thus, the discussion shows that the given valuation $| \ |_k$ can be extended to K and that we may view the value group $|k^*|_k$ as a subgroup of the extended value group, and the residue class field V_k/P_k as a subfield of the extended residue class field.

Summarizing just part of this, we have:

Theorem 1.2. If k is a field with an arbitrary non-archimedian valuation $| \ |$, and if K is an arbitrary extension field of K, then $| \ |$ can be extended to K.

Now, let us consider a non-archimedian rank one valuation $| \ |$ on k, so $|k|$ can be considered as a subgroup of the additive group of real numbers. Again, let K be an extension field of k. We want to see if it is possible to extend $| \ |$ to K so that the extended valuation is also of rank one. We shall see that this can be done if K is a finite extension of k. Before proving this, two concepts will be introduced.

Let $| \ |$ be a non-archimedian valuation of k with associated place φ and valuation ring V_k, with non-units P_k. Let $| \ |$ denote also its extension to K with associated place ψ and valuation ring V_K, with non-units P_K where K is an arbitrary extension field of k. Then, as noted in the discussion prior to Theorem 1.2, $|k^*|$, can be considered as a subgroup of $|K^*|$, and $\varphi(V_k) \simeq V_k/P_k$ as a subfield of $\psi(V_K) \simeq V_K/P_K$.

Definition 1.1. The index, $e = [|K^*| : |k^*|]$, is called the *ramification index*, and the degree, f, of the field $\psi(V_K) \simeq V_K/P_K$ over $\varphi(V_k) \simeq V_k/P_k$ is called the *residue class degree*.

In order to settle the question raised before the definition, we shall first establish the following inequality between e, f and the degree n of a finite extension field of k.

Theorem 1.3. If K is a finite extension field of degree n of k, then both e and f are finite, and $ef \leqslant n$.

Proof. Let x_1, x_2, ..., x_i be elements of V_K such that $\psi(x_1)$, $\psi(x_2)$, ..., $\psi(x_i)$ are linearly independent over $\varphi(V_k)$. Also, let y_1, y_2, ..., y_j be elements of K^* such that $|y_1| |k^*|$, $|y_2| |k^*|$, ..., $|y_j| |k^*|$ are distinct cosets of $|k^*|$ in $|K^*|$. If we can show that the ij elements $x_\nu y_u$, $\nu = 1, ..., i$, $\mu = 1, ..., j$ of K are linearly independent over k, then we shall have that $ij \leqslant n$, which implies that e and f are finite and $ef \leqslant n$. Now, let us show that these elements are, indeed, linearly independent over k.

Let $a_\nu \in k$, $\nu = 1, ..., i$. We claim that

$$| a_1 x_1 + a_2 x_2 + \cdots + a_i x_i | = \max_\nu | a_\nu |. \qquad (1.7)$$

This is certainly true if all the $a_\nu = 0$. If not, suppose $|a_1| = \max_\nu |a_\nu|$, and let $b_\nu = a_\nu / a_1$, $\nu = 1, ..., i$. Then $|b_\nu| \leqslant 1$, and $b_1 = 1$. To establish (1.7) it is clear that we must prove that

$$| x_1 + b_2 x_2 + \cdots + b_i x_i | = 1. \qquad (1.8)$$

Clearly, $| x_1 + b_2 x_2 + \cdots + b_i x_i | \leqslant 1$ since $x_1 + b_2 x_2 + \cdots + b_i x_i \in V_K$. If it were <1, then

$$\psi(x_1 + b_2 x_2 + \cdots + b_i x_i) = 0,$$

which implies that

$$\psi(x_1) + \psi(b_2) \psi(x_2) + \cdots + \psi(b_i) \psi(x_i) = 0,$$

or

$$\psi(x_1) + \varphi(b_2) \psi(x_2) + \cdots + \varphi(b_i) \psi(x_i) = 0,$$

and this is a contradiction of the assumed linear independence of $\psi(x_1)$, ..., $\psi(x_i)$. Therefore, (1.7) has been established.

Finally, suppose that

$$\sum_{\nu, \mu} c_{\nu\mu} x_\nu y_\mu = 0, \qquad (1.9)$$

where the $c_{\nu\mu} \in k$. Equation (1.9) can be written as

$$\sum_{\mu} \left(\sum_{\nu} c_{\nu\mu} x_{\nu} \right) y_{\mu} = 0. \tag{1.10}$$

Now, $|\sum_{\nu} c_{\nu\mu} x_{\nu}| \, |y_{\mu}| = 0$ or belongs to $|y_{\mu}| \, |k^*|$ by (1.7). Since the $|y_{\mu}| \, |k^*|$ are distinct, the nonzero terms of (1.10) have different valuations. Thus, if some $|\sum_{\nu} c_{\nu\mu} x_{\nu}| \, |y_{\mu}| \neq 0$, then

$$\left| \sum_{\mu} \left(\sum_{\nu} c_{\nu\mu} x_{\nu} \right) y_{\mu} \right| = \max_{\mu} \left| \sum_{\nu} c_{\nu\mu} x_{\nu} \right| \, |y_{\mu}| \neq 0,$$

which contradicts (1.10). Hence, all $|\sum_{\nu} c_{\nu\mu} x_{\nu}| \, |y_{\mu}| = 0$, i.e., all $|\sum_{\nu} c_{\nu\mu} x_{\nu}| = 0$. However, again by (1.7),

$$0 = \left| \sum_{\nu} c_{\nu\mu} x_{\nu} \right| = \max_{\nu} |c_{\nu\mu}|.$$

Thus all the $c_{\nu\mu} = 0$, and the $x_{\nu} y_{\mu}$ are linearly independent. This completes the proof.

Now, we can prove:

Theorem 1.4. If $|\,|$ is a non-archimedian rank one valuation of k, and if K is a finite extension field of k, then $|\,|$ can be extended to a rank one valuation of K.

Proof. By Theorem 1.2, $|\,|$ on k can be extended to K. We denote the extended valuation by $|\,|$ also. We also know that $|k^*| \subset |K^*|$ and that $|k^*| \subset R$. Finally, by Theorem 1.3, we have that $[|K^*| : |k^*|] = e$ is finite. $|\,|^e$ is clearly an equivalent valuation of K, and, for $\alpha \in K$,

$$|\alpha|^e \in |k^*| \subset R.$$

Thus, we have obtained an equivalent valuation with values in R. Hence, $(|\alpha|^e)^{1/e}$ (where we extract the eth root in R) is an equivalent valuation with values in R, and for $\alpha \in k$, it coincides with $|\alpha|$. This completes the proof.

There is now just one further matter which we wish to discuss concerning the extension of non-archimedian valuations $|\ |$ of rank one on a field k. We have seen, in general, by Theorems 1.1 and 1.2, that, if k is complete with respect to $|\ |$ and if K is a finite extension field of k, the extension of $|\ |$ to K is unique. Now, suppose however that k is not complete with respect to $|\ |$. In how many ways can we extend $|\ |$ to K? We shall first show that there are only finitely many extensions, and then, in the next section, we shall determine just how many there are. To show that there are just finitely many extensions, we shall prove an extended version of Theorem 1.3 for rank one valuations. Although, the theorem we shall prove is also true for arbitrary non-archimedian valuations the proof is much harder, and we refer the reader to Zariski and Samuel [23] or to Roquette [18] for the details.

Theorem 1.5. Let k be a field with a nontrivial, non-archimedian rank one valuation, $|\ |$, and let K be a finite extension field of degree n of k. Finally, let $|\ |_1$, $|\ |_2$, ... be distinct valuations of K which extend $|\ |$. If e_1, e_2, ... and f_1, f_2, ... are the respective ramification indices and residue class degrees, then $\sum e_k f_k \leqslant n$.

Proof. First observe that the valuations $|\ |_1$, $|\ |_2$, ... are not equivalent. Let $a \in k$ be such that $|a| \neq 1$, and $|a| \neq 0$. If If $|\ |_i^\alpha = |\ |_j$, then, since $|\ |_i$ and $|\ |_j$ extend $|\ |$, we would have $|a|^\alpha = |a|$, which implies that $\alpha = 1$, and $|\ |_i = |\ |_j$, a contradiction. Also, in virtue of Theorem 1.4, we may assume that the $|\ |_i$ are rank one valuations.

To the given valuation $|\ |_k$, we choose elements x_{1k}, x_{2k}, ..., $x_{f_k k}$ and elements y_{1k}, y_{2k}, ..., $y_{e_k k}$ as in the proof of Theorem 1.3. Next, by the approximation theorem of I, 3, we can find for each k and each i and j elements α_{1k}, α_{2k}, ..., $\alpha_{f_k k}$ and elements β_{1k}, β_{2k}, ..., $\beta_{e_k k}$ such that

$$|\beta_{jk} - y_{jk}|_k < |y_{jk}|_k \tag{1.11}$$
$$|\beta_{jk}|_s < \min_{r,t} |y_{rt}|_t \quad \text{for all} \quad s \neq k,$$

and

$$|\alpha_{ik} - x_{ik}|_k < 1$$
$$|\alpha_{ik}|_s < 1 \quad \text{for all} \quad s \neq k. \tag{1.12}$$

Now,

$$|\beta_{jk}|_k = |y_{jk} - (y_{jk} - \beta_{jk})|_k = |y_{jk}|_k$$

by (1.11), and, since the y_{jk} were chosen such that the cosets $|y_{jk}|_k |k^*|$ are distinct, we have that the $|\beta_{jk}|_k$ $(j = 1, ..., e_k)$ are in distinct cosets of $|k^*|$ in $|K^*|$. Also, we claim that the elements $\psi_k(\alpha_{ik})$, $i = 1, ..., f_k$ are linearly independent over $\varphi(V_k)$, where ψ_k, of course, denotes the place associated with $|\ |_k$. This follows from (1.12) since $|\alpha_{ik} - x_{ik}|_k < 1$ implies that $\psi_k(\alpha_{ik} - x_{ik}) = 0$, so

$$\psi_k(\alpha_{ik}) = \psi_k(x_{ik}),$$

and the $\psi_k(x_{ik})$ were chosen to be linearly independent over $\varphi(V_k)$.

We shall now show that the elements

$$\alpha_{ik}\beta_{jk} \tag{1.13}$$

are linearly independent over k. Once this has been shown, since (1.13) constitutes $\sum e_k f_k$ elements, it follows that $\sum e_k f_k \leqslant n$, and the theorem will have been proved. Thus, suppose that

$$\sum_{i,j,k} a_{ijk}\alpha_{ik}\beta_{jk} = 0, \tag{1.14}$$

where the $a_{ijk} \in k$. We may assume that $|a_{111}| = \max_{i,j,k}|a_{ijk}|$, and we write (1.14) as follows:

$$\sum_j \left(\sum_i a_{ij1}\alpha_{i1} \right) \beta_{j1} + \sum_{i,j,k \geqslant 2} a_{ijk}\alpha_{ik}\beta_{jk} = 0. \tag{1.15}$$

Recalling (1.7) of Theorem 1.3 and its proof, we have

$$\left| \left(\sum_i a_{i11}\alpha_{i1} \right) \beta_{11} \right|_1 = \max_i |a_{i11}| \, |\beta_{11}|_1$$

$$= |a_{111}| \, |\beta_{11}|_1 .$$

Therefore, since, as noted, the $|\beta_{j1}|_1$ are in distinct cosets of $|k^*|$

$$\left| \sum_j \left(\sum_i a_{ij1}\alpha_{i1} \right) \beta_{j1} \right|_1 = \max_j \left| \left(\sum_i a_{ij1}\alpha_{i1} \right) \beta_{j1} \right|_1$$

$$\geqslant |a_{111}| \, |\beta_{11}|_1 .$$

Next, consider the second sum in (1.15). For $k \geqslant 2$,

$$|a_{ijk}| \leqslant |a_{111}|,$$

and

$$|\alpha_{ik}|_1 < 1 \qquad \text{[by (1.12)]},$$

and

$$|\beta_{jk}|_1 < |\beta_{11}|_1 \qquad \text{[by (1.11)]}.$$

Thus,

$$|a_{ijk}| \, |\alpha_{ik}|_1 \, |\beta_{jk}|_1 < |a_{111}| \, |\beta_{11}|_1 .$$

Therefore,

$$0 = \left| \sum_{i,j,k} a_{ijk}\alpha_{ik}\beta_{jk} \right|_1 = \left| \sum_j \left(\sum_i a_{ij1}\alpha_{i1} \right) \beta_{j1} \right|_1$$

$$\geqslant |a_{111}| \, |\beta_{11}|_1 .$$

Hence, $|a_{111}| = 0$, and it follows that $|a_{ijk}| = 0$, or $a_{ijk} = 0$ for all i, j, k, which completes the proof.

It follows immediately from the theorem that there can be at most n extensions of $|\,|$ on k to K.

As the final consideration of this section, we shall discuss the problem of extending an archimedian valuation $|\,|$ on k. Suppose for the moment that k is complete with respect to $|\,|$. Consider the field $k(i)$ where i is a root of the equation $x^2 + 1 = 0$. If the valuation can be extended to $k(i)$, we know it is unique by Theorem 1.1. In fact, for $\alpha \in k(i)$, $\alpha = a + ib$, and

$$|\alpha| = \sqrt{|N(\alpha)|} = \sqrt{a^2 + b^2}. \tag{1.16}$$

But it is readily seen that (1.16), indeed, defines a valuation of $k(i)$ extending the given one, for clearly $|\alpha| \geqslant 0$ and $= 0$ if and only if $\alpha = 0$. Also,

$$|\alpha\beta| = \sqrt{|N(\alpha\beta)|} = \sqrt{N(\alpha)N(\beta)} = \sqrt{N(\alpha)}\sqrt{N(\beta)} = |\alpha||\beta|,$$

and, finally, a straight forward computation shows that

$$|\alpha + \beta| \leqslant |\alpha| + |\beta|.$$

Now, let $|\ |$ be an archimedian valuation of the field k. Then k must have characteristic 0 (see I, Exercise 5). Thus, k contains an isormorphic replica of Q, and $|\ |$ restricted to Q is equivalent to the ordinary absolute value. By replacing $|\ |$ by a suitable power, we may assume that $|\ |$ is the customary absolute value on Q. We designate, as usual, by $\hat{k}$, the completion of k. Then we have:

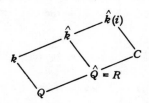

The valuation of $\hat{k}$ can be extended uniquely to $\hat{k}(i)$ as we have just noted and is a norm on $\hat{k}(i)$. Also, $\hat{k}(i)$ is complete by IV, Theorem 1.3. Hence, $\hat{k}(i)$ is a commutative Banach algebra which is a field. Therefore, $\hat{k}(i) \simeq C$ by IV, Theorem 3.7; whence k is isomorphic to a subfield of C. Thus, we have shown:

Theorem 1.6. Any field k with an archimedian valuation is isomorphic to a subfield of the field of complex numbers, and the valuation of k, viewed as a subfield of C, is a power of the usual absolute value.

If K is a finite extension field of k, and $|\ |$ an archimedian valuation of k, then k, as we have just seen, is isomorphic to a subfield of C. Since C is algebraically closed, K is also isomorphic to a subfield of C. Mapping K isomorphically into C by an isomorphism which agrees with the given one on k, gives rise clearly to an extension of the valuation on k to K. There are only finitely many such isomorphisms, and, hence, only finitely many extensions of the given non-archimedian valuation. We shall go into these matters in more detail in the next section and shall work out a number of specific examples.

2. The Number of Extensions of a Valuation

Let k be a field with a nontrivial rank one valuation, $|\ |$. Let $\hat{k}$ denote the completion of k with respect to $|\ |$. We first establish the following preliminary result.

Theorem 2.1. Let K be a finite extension field of k, and let $|\ |$ be a rank one valuation on k. Denote an extension of $|\ |$ to K again by $|\ |$. Then $\hat{K} = K\hat{k}$, where $K\hat{k}$ is the composite field formed in $\hat{K}$.

Proof.   Clearly $K\hat{k}$ is a finite extension field of $\hat{k}$, and, since $\hat{k}$ is complete, $K\hat{k}$ is also complete by IV, Theorem 1.3. Now, since $K \subset K\hat{k}$ and since K is dense in $\hat{K}$, we have $\hat{K} \subset K\hat{k}$; whence $K\hat{k} = \hat{K}$, which completes the proof.

Let K_1 and K_2 be two finite extensions of $\hat{k}$, and let $\sigma : K_1 \to K_2$ be an isomorphism of K_1 onto K_2 which leaves $\hat{k}$ fixed. The valuation $|\ |$ in $\hat{k}$ can be extended uniquely to $|\ |_1$ on K_1 and uniquely to $|\ |_2$ on K_2. We claim, that under these conditions, that, for any $\alpha \in K_1$, $|\ \alpha\ |_1 = |\ \sigma(\alpha)\ |_2$, i.e., σ takes the valuation of K_1 into the valuation of K_2. This fact is clear since, if n is the degree of these fields over $\hat{k}$,

$$| \alpha |_1 = \sqrt[n]{| N(\alpha) |} = \sqrt[n]{| N(\sigma(\alpha)) |} = | \sigma(\alpha) |_2 . \quad (2.1)$$

because σ is an isomorphism leaving $\hat{k}$ fixed.

Again, let k be a field with a rank one valuation, $|\ |$, and let K be a finite extension field of k. If $\hat{k}$ is the completion of k, we designate by $\bar{k}$, the algebraic closure of $\hat{k}$. Since $\hat{k}$ is complete, $|\ |$

can be extended to $\bar{k}$ uniquely, for, if $\alpha \in \bar{k}$, then $\hat{k}(\alpha)$ is finite of degree n, say, over $\hat{k}$, and we define

$$| \alpha | = \sqrt[n]{| N(\alpha) |}, \tag{2.2}$$

where the $N(\alpha) = N_{\hat{k}(\alpha)|\hat{k}}(\alpha)$. It is easy to see that (2.2) defines a valuation on $\bar{k}$, which extends $| \,|$ on k, and is unique. The uniqueness is clear, while clearly $| \alpha | \geqslant 0$ and $= 0$ if and only if $\alpha = 0$. Moreover, it does not matter what finite extension field containing $\hat{k}(\alpha)$ we compute $| \alpha |$ in, namely, if $\bar{k} \supset F \supset \hat{k}(\alpha)$, where F is of degree m over $\hat{k}(\alpha)$, then computing $| \alpha |$ in F gives

$$| \alpha | = \sqrt[nm]{| N_{F|\hat{k}}(\alpha) |},$$

but $N_{F|\hat{k}}(\alpha) = (N_{\hat{k}(\alpha)|\hat{k}})^m$, and the result follows. Now, if $\alpha, \beta \in \bar{k}$, we can compute $| \alpha\beta |$ and $| \alpha + \beta |$ in $\hat{k}(\alpha, \beta)$ to check the remaining axioms, and, since $| \,|$ is a valuation of $\hat{k}(\alpha, \beta)$, this completes the proof.

We can extend $| \,|$ to K if we isomorphically embed K in $\bar{k}$ by an isomorphism leaving k fixed, namely, if

$$\lambda : \quad K \to K_1 \subset \bar{k},$$

where λ on k is the identity, then let $| \,|_1$ be the restriction of $| \,|$ given by (2.2) to K_1, and, for $\beta \in K$, define

$$| \beta |_1' = | \lambda(\beta) |_1. \tag{2.3}$$

Clearly $| \,|_1'$ is a valuation of K which extends $| \,|$ on k and is *induced* by the embedding.

If

$$\lambda_1 : \quad K \to K_1 \subset \bar{k},$$

and

$$\lambda_2 : \quad K \to K_2 \subset \bar{k}$$

are two embeddings leaving k fixed, and if σ is an automorphism of $\bar{k}$ which leaves $\hat{k}$ fixed and is such that $\sigma\lambda_1 = \lambda_2$, then, by (2.1) and (2.3), for $\beta \in K$

$$| \beta |_1' = | \lambda_1(\beta) |_1 = | \sigma\lambda_1(\beta) |_2 = | \lambda_2(\beta) |_2 = | \beta |_2',$$

provided that K_1 and K_2 are extension fields of $\hat{k}$; otherwise, we consider $K_1\hat{k} = \hat{K}_1$ and $K_2\hat{k} = \hat{K}_2$. Two embeddings related as above are called *conjugate* over $\hat{k}$, and we have shown that conjugate embeddings induce the same valuations on K.

The converse of this statement is also true, for, suppose $|\ |_1' = |\ |_2'$ where $|\ |_1'$ is induced by $\lambda_1 : K \to K_1$ and $|\ |_2'$ is induced by $\lambda_2 : K \to K_2$. Then $\lambda_3 = \lambda_2\lambda_1^{-1} : K_1 \to K_2$, and λ_3 is identity on k since both λ_1 and λ_2 are. Now, we show that λ_3 can be extended to an isomorphism of $K_1\hat{k}$, the completion of K_1, onto $K_2\hat{k}$, the completion of K_2, leaving $\hat{k}$ fixed. Let $\alpha \in K_1\hat{k}$; then

$$\alpha = \lim \alpha_n, \tag{2.4}$$

where the $\alpha_n \in K_1$, and where the limit exists with respect to the valuation $|\ |_1$. However, since $|\ |_1' = |\ |_2'$, we have

$$
\begin{aligned}
|\ \lambda_3(\alpha_n) - \lambda_3(\alpha_m)\ |_2 &= |\ \lambda_3(\alpha_n - \alpha_m)\ |_2 \\
&= |\ \lambda_2\lambda_1^{-1}(\alpha_n - \alpha_m)\ |_2 \\
&= |\ \lambda_1^{-1}(\alpha_n - \alpha_m)\ |_2' \\
&= |\ \lambda_1^{-1}(\alpha_n - \alpha_m)\ |_1' \\
&= |\ \alpha_n - \alpha_m\ |_1 .
\end{aligned}
$$

Thus, $\{\lambda_3(\alpha_n)\}$ is a Cauchy sequence of $K_2\hat{k}$, and, therefore, converges to an element of $K_2\hat{k}$, which we denote by $\bar{\lambda}_3(\alpha)$. If we also have $\alpha = \lim \beta_n$, where the $\beta_n \in K_1$, and where the limit again exists in the $|\ |_1$ valuation, then, as above,

$$|\ \lambda_3(\beta_n) - \lambda_3(\alpha_n)\ |_2 = |\ \beta_n - \alpha_n\ |_1 ,$$

which shows that $\bar{\lambda}_3(\alpha)$ is independent of the sequence in (2.4). Hence,

$$\bar{\lambda}_3 : \quad K_1\hat{k} \to K_2\hat{k}$$

is well defined. It is an isomorphism, for if $\alpha = \lim \alpha_n$, and $\beta = \lim \beta_n$, then $\alpha\beta = \lim \alpha_n\beta_n$, and

$$|\ \bar{\lambda}_3(\alpha\beta) - \lambda_3(\alpha_n\beta_n)\ |_2 = |\ \bar{\lambda}_3(\alpha\beta) - \lambda_3(\alpha_n)\,\lambda_3(\beta_n)\ |_2 ,$$

but $\lambda_3(\alpha_n) \to \bar\lambda_3(\alpha)$, and $\lambda_3(\beta_n) \to \bar\lambda_3(\beta)$. Hence, $\bar\lambda_3(\alpha\beta) = \bar\lambda_3(\alpha)\bar\lambda_3(\beta)$. Similarly $\bar\lambda_3$ preserves sums. If $\bar\lambda_3(\alpha) = 0$, then

$$| \alpha_n |_1 = | \lambda_3(\alpha_n) |_2 \to 0,$$

and $\alpha = 0$. Also, if β is any element of $K_2\hat{k}$, then $\beta = \lim \beta_n$ where the $\beta_n \in K_2$. Let $\lambda_3^{-1}(\beta_n) = \alpha_n$. Then

$$| \alpha_n - \alpha_m |_1 = | \lambda_3(\alpha_n) - \lambda_3(\alpha_m) |_2$$
$$= | \beta_n - \beta_m |_2 ,$$

so $\{\alpha_n\}$ is a Cauchy sequence in $K_1\hat{k}$. Hence, $\alpha_n \to \alpha \in K_1\hat{k}$, and $\lambda_3(\alpha_n) \to \bar\lambda_3(\alpha)$, but

$$| \lambda_3(\alpha_n) - \bar\lambda_3(\alpha) |_2 = | \beta_n - \bar\lambda_3(\alpha) |_2 ,$$

so $\beta = \bar\lambda_3(\alpha)$. Thus $\bar\lambda_3$ is onto.

Next, we note that $\bar\lambda_3$ is identity on $\hat{k}$ since λ_3 is identity on k. Finally, $\bar\lambda_3$ can be extended to an automorphism of $\bar{k}$.

Therefore, we have shown that two embeddings induce the same valuation of K if and only if they are conjugate over $\hat{k}$.

Next, we show that every extension of $| \ |$ to K can be obtained by embedding K in $\bar{\hat{k}}$. Thus let $| \ |$ be a valuation of K extending the given one on k. Then, by Theorem 2.1 of this section we have:

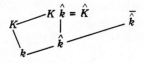

Since $\hat{K}$ is finite over $\hat{k}$, $\hat{K}$ can be extended to an algebraically closed field which is isomorphic to $\bar{\hat{k}}$ by an isomorphism leaving $\hat{k}$ fixed. This isomorphism takes $\hat{K}$ into a subfield $\hat{K}_1$ of $\bar{\hat{k}}$ and takes, according to the discussion preceding (2.1), the valuation of $\hat{K}$ into that of $\hat{K}_1$, or, in other words, the valuation of $\hat{K}$ and, therefore, of K is induced by that of $\hat{K}_1 \subset \bar{\hat{k}}$.

We summarize all this in the following theorem.

Theorem 2.2. Let k be a field with a rank one valuation, $| \ |$, and let K be a finite extension field of k. If $\hat{k}$ is the completion of k, then the set of distinct extensions of $| \ |$ to K is in one-one correspondence with those embeddings of K in $\bar{\hat{k}}$, the algebraic closure of $\hat{k}$, which are not conjugate over $\hat{k}$.

We consider now a special case, namely, let K be a finite separable extension of k. Then $K = k(\alpha)$. If $f(x)$ is the irreducible polynomial satisfied by α over k, then over $\hat{k}$

$$f(x) = p_1(x)\, p_2(x) \cdots p_r(x),$$

where the $p_i(x) \in \hat{k}[x]$ and are irreducible. Also, the $p_i(x)$ are distinct since α is separable. If λ is an embedding of $k(\alpha)$ in $\bar{\hat{k}}$, then we have:

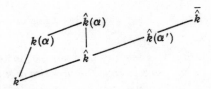

where $\lambda(\alpha) = \alpha'$. Since

$$0 = f(\alpha) = p_1(\alpha)\, p_2(\alpha) \cdots p_r(\alpha),$$
$$0 = f(\alpha') = p_1(\alpha')\, p_2(\alpha') \cdots p_r(\alpha').$$

Hence, some $p_i(\alpha') = 0$, and the embedding determines uniquely, by the separability, a polynomial $p_i(x)$.

Conversely, if we choose a polynomial $p_i(x)$ and a root α' and form $\hat{k}(\alpha')$ within $\bar{\hat{k}}$, then, since $f(\alpha') = 0$, $k(\alpha')$ and $k(\alpha)$ are isomorphic over k. α', therefore, determines an embedding of $k(\alpha)$ into $\hat{k}(\alpha') \subset \bar{\hat{k}}$. If we take a different root β' of $p_i(x)$, then we get $\hat{k}(\beta')$ which is isomorphic to $\hat{k}(\alpha')$ over $\hat{k}$ since α' and β' are roots of the same irreducible polynomial over $\hat{k}$. These would then determine conjugate embeddings of $k(\alpha)$ in $\bar{\hat{k}}$, and hence, as we know, the same valuation of $k(\alpha)$.

We also see that

$$n = \sum_{i=1}^{r} n_i , \tag{2.5}$$

where $n = $ degree of $f(x) = $ degree of K over $k = $ the *global degree*, and $n_i =$ degree of $p_i(x) =$ degree $\hat{k}(\alpha')$ over $\hat{k}$ [where α' is a root of $p_i(x)$] $=$ the *local degree*.

Thus, we have shown:

Theorem 2.3. If $K = k(\alpha)$ is a finite separable extension of k, and if $|\ |$ is a rank one valuation of k, then there are as many distinct extensions of $|\ |$ to K as there are irreducible factors of $f(x)$ over $\hat{k}$, where $f(x)$ is the irreducible polynomial satisfied by α over k, and where $\hat{k}$ is the completion of k. Moreover, the global degree of the extension is equal to the sum of the local degrees.

If K is a finite inseparable extension, then we could decompose K into a separable extension, K_s, and a purely inseparable extension of K_s obtained by adjoining pth roots to K_s, where p is the characteristic of k. Since K_s is a finite separable extension of k, $K_s = k(\alpha)$, and we can apply Theorem 2.3 to K_s. Then we note that $|\ |$ on K_s is uniquely extendable to K, for, if $\gamma \in K_s(\delta) \subset K$ where $K_s(\delta)$ is of degree p over K_s, then $\gamma^p = \beta \in K_s$. If $|\gamma|$ is defined, then $|\gamma|^p = |\beta|$, and $|\gamma| = |\beta|^{1/p}$. Continuing in this fashion, we obtain uniqueness.

We return again to the situation where K is a finite separable extension of k, and where $|\ |$ is a rank one valuation of k. We shall look at our previous results from a slightly different point of view. Let E be the least separable normal extension of k containing K. Denote by G, the Galois group of E over k, and by U, the subgroup of G which leaves K fixed. If $|\ |$ is extended to K, then we know by the preceding discussion that there is an embedding λ_1 of K into $\hat{k}$. λ_1 leaves k fixed. Let

$$K \xrightarrow{\lambda_1} K_1 \subset \hat{k}$$

Also, we know that $|\ |$ is of the form $|\ |_1'$, and, for $\alpha \in K$,

$$|\alpha|_1' = |\lambda_1(\alpha)|_1 ,$$

where $|\ |_1$ is the unique valuation of K_1 determined by $|\ |$ on $\hat{k}$. But since λ_1 is an isomorphism of K which is the identity on k, λ_1 is given by an automorphism $\nu_1 \in G$, i.e., $\nu_1|_K = \lambda_1$. Thus

$$|\alpha|_1' = |\nu_1(\alpha)|_1 ,$$

where $\nu_1 \in G$. Also, it is clear that any $\nu \in G$ leads to an induced valuation of E and, hence, of K, for $\nu : E \to E$ can be extended to $\bar{\nu} : E\hat{k} \to E\hat{k}$, and $E\hat{k}$ can subsequently be mapped by an isomorphism over $\hat{k}$ into $\bar{k}$, so ν gives rise to an embedding in $\bar{k}$ and to a valuation on E induced by ν.

Now, let

$$K \xrightarrow{\lambda_2} K_2 \subset \hat{k}$$

be another embedding, then, as above,

$$\mid \alpha \mid_2' \; = \; \mid \nu_2(\alpha) \mid_2 \, ,$$

where $\nu_2 \in G$. We also saw that, if $\mid \; \mid_1' \; = \; \mid \; \mid_2'$, there exists an isomorphism

$$\bar{\lambda}_3 : \quad K_1\hat{k} \to K_2\hat{k}$$

such that $\bar{\lambda}_3$ is identity on $\hat{k}$, and $\bar{\lambda}_3\nu_1 = \nu_2$ on K. $\bar{\lambda}_3$ can be extended to an automorphism

$$\sigma : \quad E\hat{k} \to E\hat{k}$$

over $\hat{k}$, i.e., $\sigma \in S$, the Galois group of $E\hat{k}$ over $\hat{k}$, which by the theorem on natural irrationalities is isomorphic to the subgroup of G which has $E \cap \hat{k}$ as its fixed field. Now, σ has on K_1 the same effect as $\bar{\lambda}_3$ since σ extends $\bar{\lambda}_3$, so

$$\sigma\nu_1 = \nu_2 \qquad \text{on } K,$$

or

$$\nu_1^{-1}\sigma^{-1}\nu_2 = 1 \qquad \text{on } K.$$

Therefore,

$$\nu_1^{-1}\sigma^{-1}\nu_2 \in U,$$

or,

$$\nu_2 \in \sigma\nu_1 U,$$

and

$$\nu_2 \in S\nu_1 U.$$

Conversely, if $\nu_2 = \sigma\nu_1\mu$, where $\sigma \in S$ and $\mu \in U$, then, for $\alpha \in K$,

$$
\begin{aligned}
\mid \alpha \mid_2' &= \mid \nu_2(\alpha) \mid_2 = \mid \sigma\nu_1\mu(\alpha) \mid_2 \\
&= \mid \sigma\nu_1(\alpha) \mid_2 \\
&= \mid \nu_1(\alpha) \mid_1 \qquad \text{[by (2.1)]} \\
&= \mid \alpha \mid_1'.
\end{aligned}
$$

We have, therefore, established the following result:

Theorem 2.4. Let K be a finite separable extension of k, and let $\mid \; \mid$ be a rank one valuation of k. If E is the least separable normal extension of k containing K with Galois group G, and if U is the subgroup of G which fixes K, decompose G into distinct double cosets: $G = \bigcup_{i=1}^{r} S\nu_i U$, where S is the Galois group of $E\hat{k}$ over $\hat{k}$. Then there are as many extensions of $\mid \; \mid$ to K as there are distinct double cosets, and all of these extensions are of the form: $\mid \nu_i(\alpha) \mid_i$, $i = 1, ..., r$, where the $\mid \; \mid_i$ are the unique extensions of $\mid \; \mid$ in $\hat{k}$ to the embeddings of K in $\hat{k}$ associated with the ν_i .

We shall now apply this theorem to obtain a result, particularly useful in number theory. First, write G as a distinct union of double cosets: $G = \bigcup_i S\nu_i U$. Since

$$
S \supset S \cap \nu_i U \nu_i^{-1},
$$

we can decompose S into disjoint cosets

$$
S = \bigcup_j \sigma_{ij}(S \cap \nu_i U \nu_i^{-1}) . \tag{2.6}
$$

Hence,

$$
S\nu_i U \nu_i^{-1} = \bigcup_j \sigma_{ij}\nu_i U \nu_i^{-1} ,
$$

or

$$
S\nu_i U = \bigcup_j \sigma_{ij}\nu_i U.
$$

We claim that this last union is disjoint, for suppose that

$$
\sigma_{ij}\nu_i U = \sigma_{ik}\nu_i U \qquad (j \neq k).
$$

Then

$$\sigma_{ik}^{-1}\sigma_{ij}\nu_i \in \sigma_{ik}^{-1}\sigma_{ij}\nu_i U = \nu_i U,$$

so

$$\sigma_{ik}^{-1}\sigma_{ij}\nu_i = \nu_i\mu,$$

where $\mu \in U$. Thus,

$$\sigma_{ik}^{-1}\sigma_{ij} = \nu_i\mu\nu_i^{-1},$$

and, therefore,

$$\sigma_{ik}^{-1}\sigma_{ij} \in S \cap \nu_i U\nu_i^{-1},$$

which is a contradiction. Hence, we can write

$$G = \bigcup_{i,j} \sigma_{ij}\nu_i U \qquad \text{(disjoint)}. \tag{2.7}$$

The group of $\nu_i(K)$, where we use the same notation as in the theorem, is $\nu_i U\nu_i^{-1}$, while the group of $\nu_i(K)\,\hat{k}$ is $S \cap \nu_i U\nu_i^{-1}$. Thus the trace of $\nu_i(\alpha)$, where $\alpha \in K$, from $\nu_i(K)\,\hat{k}$ to $\hat{k}$ is given, using (2.6), by

$$S_{\nu_i(K)\hat{k}\,|\,\hat{k}}(\nu_i(\alpha)) = \sum_j \sigma_{ij}\nu_i(\alpha),$$

and the trace of α from K to k, using (2.7), is given by

$$S_{K\,|\,k}(\alpha) = \sum_{i,j} \sigma_{ij}\nu_i(\alpha).$$

Therefore, we have

$$S_{K\,|\,k}(\alpha) = \sum_i S_{\nu_i(K)\hat{k}\,|\,\hat{k}}(\nu_i(\alpha)).$$

In other words, the global trace is equal to the sum of the local traces, and, similarly,

$$N_{K\,|\,k}(\alpha) = \prod_i N_{\nu_i(K)\hat{k}\,|\,\hat{k}}(\nu_i(\alpha)),$$

or the global norm is the produce of the local norms, where all of these results have been established under the assumptions of

Theorem 2.4. One frequently abbreviates these formulas by simply writing

$$S_{K|_k}(\alpha) = \sum_i S_{K_i|_k}(\alpha),$$

and

$$N_{K|_k}(\alpha) = \prod_i N_{K_i|_k}(\alpha).$$

These results hold under somewhat broader conditions than those of the theorem, but we shall not go into such matters here.

3. Valuations of Algebraic Number Fields—Examples

If K is an algebraic number field, i.e., $K = Q(\theta)$, where θ satisfies the irreducible polynomial $f(x)$ over Q, then we can apply the results of the last section, in particular Theorems 2.2 and 2.3, along with the results of Chapter I. We know, disregarding equivalent valuations and the trivial one, that the only valuations of Q are the ordinary absolute value and the p-adic valuations. To see how these extend to K, we apply the preceding results. For example, if $|\ |$ is the ordinary absolute value, then $\hat{Q} = R$, and $f(x)$ decomposes, in general, over R into linear and quadratic factors:

$$f(x) = (x - \alpha_1) \cdots (x - \alpha_r)\, p_1(x) \cdots p_t(x).$$

The extensions of $|\ |$ to K are now obtained by considering all the non-conjugate embeddings of K in $\bar{Q} = \bar{R} = C$ determined by roots of these polynomials. These various embeddings induce all possible valuations on K extending $|\ |$ on Q, and we see that there are $r + t$ of them.

In the case of a p-adic valuation $|\ |_p$ on Q, the same sort of observations hold only now $\hat{Q} = Q_p$, and we must investigate how $f(x)$ factors over Q_p. Each irreducible factor determines an embedding of K in $\bar{Q}_p$ and induces a valuation on K extending $|\ |_p$.

We shall now consider some specific examples to see how these steps are carried out, and to see how the extended valuation is determined for various elements.

Example 1. Take $K = Q(\theta)$, where θ satisfies $x^2 + 1 = 0$; and let $|\ |$ be the usual absolute value on Q. Over R, $x^2 + 1$ is irreducible. Hence there is just one extension, $|\ |'$, of $|\ |$ to K, obtained by embedding $Q(\theta)$ in $Q(i) \subset C$ and taking the induced valuation. Thus,

$$|\, a + b\theta\, |' = |\, a + bi\, | = \sqrt{a^2 + b^2}.$$

Example 2. Let $K = Q(\theta)$, where θ satisfies the irreducible equation $x^3 = 3$, and let $|\ |$ be the usual absolute value on Q. Over R, $x^3 - 3$ factors into a linear factor $(x - \sqrt[3]{3})$ and a quadratic factor $p(x)$ with roots $\sqrt[3]{3}\epsilon$ and $\sqrt[3]{3}\epsilon^2$ in C, where ϵ is a primitive cube root of unity. There are, therefore, two extensions $|\ |_1'$ and $|\ |_2'$ of $|\ |$ to K obtained by embedding $Q(\theta)$ in $Q(\sqrt[3]{3}) \subset C$ and in $Q(\sqrt[3]{3}\epsilon) \subset C$.

For example,

$$|\, 1 - \theta\, |_1' = |\, 1 - \sqrt[3]{3}\, | = \sqrt[3]{3} - 1.$$

$$|\, 1 - \theta\, |_2' = |\, 1 - \epsilon\sqrt[3]{3}\, |.$$

Example 3. Let $K = Q(\theta)$, where θ satisfies the irreducible equation $f(x) = x^3 - x - 1$, and consider the 17-adic valuation, $|\ |_{17}$, on Q. Let $\alpha_1 = 5$; then $f(\alpha_1) = 119 = 7 \times 17$, and $f'(\alpha_1) = 74$. Thus, $|f(\alpha_1)|_{17} < 1$, and $|f'(\alpha_1)|_{17} = 1$. Therefore, by II, Theorem 4.1, the sequence

$$\alpha_1,\ \alpha_2,\ \ldots$$

of II, (4.1) converges to a root β of $f(x)$ in Q_{17}. The second term α_2, is given by

$$\alpha_2 = \alpha_1 - \frac{f(\alpha_1)}{f'(\alpha_1)}$$

$$= 5 - \frac{119}{74}$$

$$= \frac{251}{74} \equiv -63 \qquad (\bmod\ 17^2\hat{V}),$$

where $\hat{V}$ is the valuation ring of $|\ |_{17}$ on Q_{17}. We could clearly compute β to any desired degree of accuracy. Now, over Q_{17},

$$x^3 - x - 1 = (x - \beta)\, p(x),$$

where $p(x)$ is a quadratic polynomial, which we claim is irreducible over Q_{17}. In order to show this, we must just show that $p(x)$ has no root modulo 17, for if, say, $p(\alpha) = 0$, where $\alpha \in Q_{17}$, let $\alpha \equiv a \pmod{17\hat{V}}$, where $a \in Z$. Such an a exists for, if $p(\alpha) = 0$, then $\alpha^3 - \alpha - 1 = 0$, and clearly $\alpha \in \hat{V}$. Then

$$0 = p(\alpha) \equiv p(a) \qquad (\text{mod } 17\hat{V}),$$

and, since $p(a)$ is an integer,

$$p(a) \equiv 0 \qquad (\text{mod } 17).$$

Now, since $\beta \equiv 5 \ (\text{mod } 17\hat{V})$,

$$p(x) \equiv x^2 + 5x + 7 \qquad (\text{mod } 17\hat{V}), \tag{3.1}$$

and we must show that $x^2 + 5x + 7$ has no root modulo 17. But

$$\begin{aligned}
x^2 + 5x + 7 &\equiv x^2 - 12x + 7 \qquad (\text{mod } 17) \\
&\equiv (x - 6)^2 + 5 \qquad (\text{mod } 17) \\
&= y^2 + 5,
\end{aligned}$$

where $y = x - 6$. However, the congruence

$$y^2 \equiv -5 \qquad (\text{mod } 17)$$

has no solution since, by the quadratic reciprocity law,

$$\left(\frac{-5}{17}\right) = \left(\frac{-1}{17}\right)\left(\frac{5}{17}\right) = \left(\frac{5}{17}\right) = \left(\frac{17}{5}\right) = \left(\frac{2}{5}\right) = -1.$$

Thus, there are just two extensions of $|\ |_{17}$ to K obtained by embedding

$$Q(\theta) \simeq Q(\beta) \subset \bar{Q}_{17},$$

and

$$Q(\theta) \simeq Q(\gamma) \subset \bar{Q}_{17},$$

where γ is a root of $p(x)$ in $\bar{Q}_{17}$. Denote the induced valuations by $|\ |_1'$ and $|\ |_2'$, respectively. Let us compute some specific values for these two extensions. Consider the element $3 - 2\theta + 6\theta^2 \in Q(\theta)$.

$$|\ 3 - 2\theta + 6\theta^2\ |_1' = |\ 3 - 2\beta + 6\beta^2\ |_{17}.$$

But

$$3 - 2\beta + 6\beta^2 \equiv 3 - 10 + 150 = 143 \qquad (\bmod\ 17\hat{V}),$$

and since $17 \nmid 143$, we have

$$|\ 3 - 2\theta + 6\theta^2\ |_1' = 1.$$

If in this computation 17 had divided the number, we would have to go to the second approximation to β and possibly further. For example, let us compute

$$|\ 7 + 2\theta\ |_1' = |\ 7 + 2\beta\ |_{17}$$
$$7 + 2\beta \equiv 17 \qquad (\bmod\ 17\hat{V}),$$

but $\beta \equiv -63 \ (\bmod\ 17^2\hat{V})$. Thus

$$7 + 2\beta \equiv -119 \qquad (\bmod\ 17^2\hat{V}),$$

and, since $17^2 \nmid 119$, we have

$$|\ 7 + 2\theta\ |_1' = |\ 17\ |_{17}.$$

We consider next the valuation $|\ |_2'$, and compute $|\ 1 + \theta + \theta^2\ |_2'$. We denote again by $|\ |_{17}$ the unique extension of $|\ |_{17}$ to $Q_{17}(\gamma)$. Then

$$|\ 1 + \theta + \theta^2\ |_2' = |\ 1 + \gamma + \gamma^2\ |_{17}.$$

From (3.1), we have

$$\gamma^2 \equiv -5\gamma - 7 \qquad (\bmod\ 17\hat{V}).$$

Thus,

$$1 + \gamma + \gamma^2 \equiv -4\gamma - 6 \qquad (\bmod\ 17\hat{V}),$$

and $|\ 4\gamma + 6\ |_{17} = |\ 2\gamma + 3\ |_{17}$.

Now, the norm of $2\gamma + 3$ is, denoting the other root of $p(x)$ in $\bar{Q}_{17}$ by γ',

$$
\begin{aligned}
N(2\gamma + 3) &= (2\gamma + 3)(2\gamma' + 3) \\
&= 9 + 6(\gamma + \gamma') + 4\gamma\gamma' \\
&\equiv 9 - 30 + 28 = 7 \qquad (\mathrm{mod}\ 17\hat{V}).
\end{aligned}
$$

Therefore,

$$
|\, 2\gamma + 3\, |_{17} = \sqrt{|\, 7\, |_{17}} = 1;
$$

hence, also

$$
|\, 1 + \theta + \theta^2\, |_{2}{}' = 1.
$$

If we had obtained a number divisible by 17, then, as in the preceding computation, we would have to go to higher approximations.

Example 4. Let $K = Q(\theta)$, where θ satisfies the irreducible equation $f(x) = x^3 - 2x + 2$, and consider $|\ |_{23}$ on Q. For $\alpha_1 = 3$, we get $|f(\alpha_1)|_{23} < 1$ and $|f'(\alpha_1)|_{23} = 1$. Similarly for $\alpha_1 = 9$ and $\alpha_1 = 11$. Hence, we get three distinct roots α, β, γ in Q_{23} such that

$$
\begin{aligned}
\alpha &\equiv 3 \qquad (23\hat{V}) \\
\beta &\equiv 9 \qquad (23\hat{V}) \\
\gamma &\equiv 11 \qquad (23\hat{V}).
\end{aligned}
$$

Thus, there are three extensions of $|\ |_{23}$ to K.

Example 5. We now consider $K = Q(\theta)$, where θ satisfies the same irreducible equation $f(x)$ as in Example 4, namely, $f(x) = x^3 - 2x + 2$, but we consider $|\ |_2$ on Q instead of $|\ |_{23}$ as in Example 4. If we take $\alpha_1 = 0$, then $f(\alpha_1) = 2$, and $|f(\alpha_1)|_2 < 1$. However, $f'(\alpha_1) = -2$, and $|f'(\alpha_1)|_2 < 1$, while $d_1 = \frac{1}{2}$, so $|d_1|_2 > 1$. Therefore, neither version of Newton's theorem in Chapter II can be applied. If we take $\alpha_1 = 1$, then $|f(\alpha_1)|_2 = 1$, and, again, we can not apply Newton's method to see if $f(x)$ factors over Q_2. Instead we argue as follows:

$$
\theta^3 - 2\theta + 2 = 0;
$$

hence, if $|\ |$ denotes an extension of $|\ |_2$ to K, we see, first of all from this equation, that $|\ \theta\ | < 1$. Secondly, we see that there must be more than one dominant term, for we know, in general, in the case of non-archimedean valuations that if $|\ \alpha\ | < |\ \beta\ |$, then $|\ \alpha + \beta\ | = |\ \beta\ |$. Since $|\ \theta\ | < 1$, $|\ 2\theta\ | < |\ 2\ |$, and we must have

$$|\ \theta\ |^3 = |\ 2\ | = |\ 2\ |_2,$$

or

$$|\ \theta\ | = |\ 2\ |_2^{1/3}.$$

This implies that the ramification index for this extension is at least 3. However, the degree of $Q(\theta)$ over Q is 3. Thus, we get that there is just one extension of $|\ |_2$ to $Q(\theta)$ with ramification index 3 and residue class degree 1.

We leave the examples now, but we note that the computations performed here are particularly important in number theory. One is concerned there, among other things, with the factorization of primes of Z in the ring of integers of algebraic extension fields, and this is intimately related to the extension of a given p-adic valuation. We also observe that the two cases considered in Examples 4 and 5 behaved quite differently. This can be traced to a consideration of the discriminant of the equation. In general, for the cubic equation $x^3 + px + q$, the discriminant $D = -4p^3 - 27q^2$, which in our case is -4×19, so $2 \mid D$, while $23 \nmid D$. These considerations are related to the ramification problem for primes in number theory, but we cannot go into these matters here.

4. Discrete Valuations

We shall briefly discuss in this section some properties of discrete valuations. Many of the properties will be just extensions of results already obtained for the p-adic valuations, which are examples of discrete valuations. We assume throughout that k is a field with a non-archimedean valuation $|\ |$.

Definition 4.1. The valuation $|\ |$ is called *discrete* if its value group $|\ k^*\ |$ is an infinite cyclic group.

If $|\ |$ is a discrete valuation of k, then $|\ k^*\ |$ is an infinite cyclic group and is, therefore, order isomorphic to Z. Hence, there exists a $\pi \in k$ such that $|\ \pi\ | < 1$, and $|\ \pi\ |$ generates $|\ k^*\ |$. It is clear that $|\ \pi\ |$ is the maximum of all $|\ a\ |$, $a \in k$, such that $|\ a\ | < 1$. Given any $a \in k^*$, $a \neq 0$, there exists an integer, as in the case of the p-adic valuations, called the ordinal of a and denoted by ord a such that

$$|\ a\ | = |\ \pi\ |^{\mathrm{ord}a}.$$

Thus, $a = \pi^{\mathrm{ord}a}\epsilon$, where $|\ \epsilon\ | = 1$, so ϵ is a unit. For $a = 0$, we take ord $a = \infty$. Then

$$|\ a\ | = 1 \Leftrightarrow \mathrm{ord}\ a = 0,$$
$$|\ a\ | < 1 \Leftrightarrow \mathrm{ord}\ a > 0,$$
$$|\ a\ | > 1 \Leftrightarrow \mathrm{ord}\ a < 0.$$

We also have that

$$\mathrm{ord}\ ab = \mathrm{ord}\ a + \mathrm{ord}\ b,$$

and

$$\mathrm{ord}\ (a + b) \geqslant \min\ (\mathrm{ord}\ a, \mathrm{ord}\ b).$$

If V is the associated valuation ring with P, the maximal ideal of non-units, it is clear that

$$P = \{a \mid \mathrm{ord}\ a \geqslant 1\} = \pi V.$$

Also, π is a prime element of the ring V, for, if $\pi = \alpha_1\alpha_2$ where α_1, $\alpha_2 \in V$, then, since $|\ \pi\ | < 1$, either $|\ \alpha_1\ | < 1$, or $|\ \alpha_2\ | < 1$. If, say, $|\ \alpha_1\ | < 1$, then $\alpha_1 \in P = \pi V$, and $\pi \mid \alpha_1$, but $\alpha_1 \nmid \pi$; whence, π is a prime.

Now, let K be a finite extension field of k, and let $|\ |$ be extended to K. We shall denote the extension also by $|\ |$, and we claim that this extended valuation in K is also discrete, namely:

Theorem 4.1. If K is a finite extension field of k, and if $|\ |$ is a discrete valuation of k, then any extension of $|\ |$ to K is also discrete.

Proof. We know by Theorem 1.3 of this chapter that if n is the degree of the extension, $ef \leqslant n$ where e is the ramification index and f, the residue class degree of the extension. Then

$$| K^* |^e \subset | k^* |.$$

Thus, we have a mapping

$$| K^* | \rightarrow | k^* |$$

given by $| \alpha | \rightarrow | \alpha |^e$ where $\alpha \in K^*$. The mapping is an isomorphism into $| k^* |$, for it is readily seen to be a homomorphism, while, if $| \alpha |^e = 1$, then it follows immediately since $| k^* |$ is ordered that $| \alpha | = 1$. Thus, the ordered group $| K^* |$ is isomorphic to a subgroup of the ordered infinite cyclic group $| k^* |$, and, therefore, must be infinite cyclic also. This completes the proof.

Again, we assume that K is a finite extension of k and that $| \ |$ is a discrete valuation of k which has been extended to K. We denote the extension also by $| \ |$, and we let e be the ramification index of the extension. Finally, let $| \pi |$ be the generator of $| k^* |$ with $| \pi | < 1$, and $| \Pi |$ the generator of $| K^* |$ with $| \Pi | < 1$. Since $| \pi | < 1$

$$\pi = \epsilon \Pi^n,$$

where n is a positive integer and where ϵ is a unit of K. However, $| K^* | = [| \Pi |]$, the cyclic group generated by $| \Pi |$, and $| k^* | = [| \pi |]$, the cyclic group generated by $| \pi |$. Now, $| k^* | = [| \pi |] = [| \Pi |^n]$, so

$$[| K^* | : | k^* |] = n,$$

but $[| K^* | : | k^* |] = e$. Therefore, $e = n$, and

$$\pi = \epsilon \Pi^e. \tag{4.1}$$

Now, if $a \in k$, then, of course, a also belongs to K, and we can compute its ordinal with respect to π, denoted by $\mathrm{ord}_k a$, or its ordinal with respect to Π, denoted by $\mathrm{ord}_K a$. Equation (4.1) shows that

$$\mathrm{ord}_K a = e \, \mathrm{ord}_k a.$$

Next, we simply note that the extension of II, Theorem 2.1 is valid for discrete valuations; namely, if k is a complete field with respect to the discrete valuation $|\ |$, then every $\alpha \in k$ can be written in the form

$$\alpha = \sum_n^\infty \alpha_j \pi^j,$$

where $n = \operatorname{ord} \alpha$, and where the $\alpha_{j_i} \in V$, the associated valuation ring. The proof is essentially the same as that in Q_p and need not be repeated.

We now wish to show that Theorem 1.3 of this chapter can be improved if k is a complete field with respect to a discrete valuation.

Theorem 4.2. Let K be a finite extension field of degree n of k, where k is complete with respect to a discrete valuation, $|\ |$, then $ef = n$.

Proof. We adhere to the same notation used prior to the statement of the theorem. Let $x_1, x_2, ..., x_f$ be elements of the valuation ring V_K associated with $|\ |$ on K such that $\psi(x_1)$, $\psi(x_2), ..., \psi(x_f)$ is a basis of $\psi(V_K)$ over $\varphi(V_K)$, where ψ is the associated place of $|\ |$ on K, and φ and V_k are, respectively, the associated place and valuation ring of $|\ |$ on k. We wish to show that every element of K is a linear combination of the elements $x_i \Pi^j$, $i = 1, ..., f$, $j = 0, 1, ..., e - 1$ with coefficients from k. Since the cosets

$$|\ k^*\ |,\ |\ \Pi\ |\ |\ k^*\ |,\ ...,\ |\ \Pi^{e-1}\ |\ |\ k^*\ |$$

are distinct, we know, by the proof of Theorem 1.3 of this chapter, that the elements $x_i \Pi^j$ are linearly independent over k. Hence, if we can prove that every element of K is a linear combination of these elements with coefficients from k, then they will form a basis of K over k, and, consequently, $ef = n$. Actually, we shall prove more; namely, we shall show that every element of

V_K is a linear combination of the $x_i \Pi^j$ with coefficients from V_k, i.e.,

$$V_K = \sum_{i,j} V_k x_i \Pi^j. \tag{4.2}$$

For suppose that (4.2) has been established. Then let $\alpha \in K$. Select an $a \in k^*$ such that $|a\alpha| \leqslant 1$. Such an a always exists, for example, some sufficiently higher power of π will work. Then

$$a\alpha \in V_K = \sum_{i,j} V_k x_i \Pi^j,$$

which implies that

$$\alpha \in \sum_{i,j} k x_i \Pi^j.$$

Thus, we must just prove (4.2).

Consider $|\pi^i \Pi^j|$, where $i = 0, 1, 2, ...,$ and $j = 0, 1, ..., e - 1$. By (4.1) we have

$$|\pi^i \Pi^j| = |\Pi^{ei+j}|,$$

but clearly $ei + j$ ranges over all non-negative integers, so $|\pi^i \Pi^j|$ yields all values of $|\ |$ on V_K. Now let $\alpha \in V_K$, $\alpha \neq 0$. Suppose that

$$|\alpha| \leqslant |\pi^i \Pi^j|$$

for some $i = 0, 1, 2, ...$ and some $j = 0, 1, ..., e - 1$. Set $\beta = \alpha / \pi^i \Pi^j$. Then $|\beta| \leqslant 1$, so $\psi(\beta) \in \psi(V_K)$. Therefore,

$$\psi(\beta) = \psi(a_1)\,\psi(x_1) + \psi(a_2)\,\psi(x_2) + \cdots + \psi(a_f)\,\psi(x_f),$$

where the $a_i \in V_k$. Hence

$$\psi(\beta) = \psi(a_1 x_1 + a_2 x_2 + \cdots + a_f x_f),$$

or

$$\psi(\beta - (a_1 x_1 + \cdots + a_f x_f)) = 0.$$

But this means that

$$|\beta - (a_1 x_1 + \cdots + a_f x_f)| < 1,$$

or, recalling the definition of β, that

$$| \alpha - (a_1 x_1 + \cdots + a_f x_f) \, \pi^i \Pi^j \, | < | \, \pi^i \Pi^j \, |.$$

Let

$$\alpha - (a_1 x_1 + \cdots + a_f x_f) \, \pi^i \Pi^j = \gamma.$$

We have, therefore, shown that, if $| \alpha | \leqslant | \pi^i \Pi^j |$, there exist elements a_1, ..., a_f in V_k and an element $\gamma \in V_K$ such that

$$\alpha = (a_1 x_1 + \cdots + a_f x_f) \, \pi^i \Pi^j + \gamma,$$

with $| \gamma | < | \pi^i \Pi^j |$.

Now let α be an arbitrary element of V_K, so $| \alpha | \leqslant 1$. By the preceding result, we can write

$$\alpha = a_{001} x_1 + a_{002} x_2 + \cdots + a_{00f} x_f + \alpha_1 \,,$$

where the $a_{00i} \in V_k$ and where $| \alpha_1 | < 1$, so $| \alpha_1 | \leqslant | \Pi |$. Similarly, considering α_1, we have

$$\alpha_1 = (a_{011} x_1 + \cdots + a_{01f} x_f) \, \Pi + \alpha_2 \,,$$

where $| \alpha_2 | < | \Pi |$, so $| \alpha_2 | \leqslant | \Pi^2 |$. Similarly,

$$\alpha_2 = (a_{021} x_1 + \cdots + a_{02f} x_f) \, \Pi^2 + \alpha_3 \,,$$

where $| \alpha_3 | \leqslant | \Pi^3 |$. Continuing, we get down to

$$\alpha_{e-1} = (a_{0e-1,1} x_1 + \cdots + a_{0e-1,f} x_f) \, \Pi^{e-1} + \alpha_e \,,$$

where $| \alpha_e | \leqslant | \Pi^e | = | \pi |$. Hence,

$$\alpha_e = (a_{101} x_1 + \cdots + a_{10f} x_f) \, \pi + \alpha_{e+1} \,,$$

where $| \alpha_{e+1} | \leqslant | \pi \Pi |$, so

$$\alpha_{e+1} = (a_{111} x_1 + \cdots + a_{11f}) \, \pi \Pi + \alpha_{e+2} \,,$$

where $| \alpha_{e+2} | \leqslant | \pi \Pi^2 |$, and so on.

Performing successive substitutions, we see that α can be written as a certain finite sum plus a small remainder term, namely,

$$\alpha = \sum_{i,j} (a_{ij1}x_1 + \cdots + a_{ijf}x_f) \, \pi^i \varPi^j + \gamma,$$

where the sum is finite and where $|\gamma|$ is arbitrarily small. Thus,

$$\alpha = \sum_{i,j} (a_{ij1}x_1 + \cdots + a_{ijf}x_f) \, \pi^i \varPi^j \qquad (4.3)$$

where $i = 0, 1, 2, \ldots,$ and $j = 0, 1, \ldots, e - 1$. We can write (4.3) in the form

$$\alpha = \sum_{j=0}^{e-1} \left(\left(\sum_i a_{ij1}\pi^i \right) x_1 + \left(\sum_i a_{ij2}\pi^i \right) x_2 + \cdots + \left(\sum_i a_{ijf}\pi^i \right) x_f \right) \varPi^j,$$

the $\sum_i a_{ijk}\pi^i$ converge since the $a_{ijk} \in V_k$ and $|a_{ijk}\pi^i| \to 0$. In fact, $\sum_i a_{ijk}\pi^i \in V_k$, since, if s_n denotes the nth partial sum, $|s_n| \leqslant 1$; whence, $|\sum_i a_{ijk}\pi^i| = \lim |s_n| \leqslant 1$, and this shows that (4.2) is true and completes the proof of the theorem.

We saw in II, Theorem 1.4 that if $|\ |$ is a non-archimedian rank one valuation on k, then $|k| = |\hat{k}|$, where $\hat{k}$, as usual, denotes the completion of k. We note that the same is true for the residue class fields, namely, the residue class field of k is the same as that of $\hat{k}$. For, if φ is the associated place, and if $\alpha \in \hat{k}$, $|\alpha| \leqslant 1$, then since k is dense in $\hat{k}$, there exists an $a \in k$ such that $|\alpha - a| < 1$, or $\alpha = a + \beta$, where $|\beta| < 1$. Hence $\varphi(\alpha) = \varphi(a)$, which establishes the contention.

Next, we observe that Theorem 4.2 is not true, in general, if $|\ |$ is not a discrete valuation even though the field k may be complete. This may be seen as follows: We start off with the field Q and the 2-adic valuation $|\ |_2$ and form the completion, Q_2. Now, form $Q_2(\sqrt{2})$. The valuation can be uniquely extended to $Q_2(\sqrt{2})$ and is given by

$$|\alpha| = \sqrt{|N(\alpha)|_2}$$

for $\alpha \in Q_2(\sqrt{2})$. Also, $Q_2(\sqrt{2})$ is complete since it is finite over

Q_2, and, by Theorem 4.1, the valuation on $Q_2(\sqrt{2})$ is discrete. Since

$$| \sqrt{2} | = | 2 |_2^{1/2},$$

we see that $e = 2$, and, since $n = ef, f = 1$. Also,

$$1 > | \sqrt{2} | > | 2 |_2 .$$

If we now form $Q_2(\sqrt{2}, \sqrt[4]{2})$, then again we have a unique extension of the valuation with $e = 2, f = 1$, and

$$1 > | \sqrt[4]{2} | > | \sqrt{2} | > | 2 |_2 .$$

We continue in this fashion and form

$$k = Q_2(\sqrt{2}, \sqrt[4]{2}, \sqrt[8]{2}, ...).$$

Since k is algebraic over Q_2, the valuation can be extended uniquely to k, but it is clearly no longer discrete. We now form the completion $\hat{k}$, and let $K = \hat{k}(\sqrt{-1})$. We claim that in this case the degree n of K over $\hat{k}$ is 2, while $e = f = 1$. Hence, $n \neq ef$ even though $\hat{k}$ is complete. First, we have that $n = 2$, for $\sqrt{-1} \notin Q_2$, and, therefore, $\sqrt{-1} \notin k$. It also does not belong to $\hat{k}$, for if $\sqrt{-1} = \lim \alpha_n$, where the $\alpha_n \in k$, then we must have $| \alpha_n | = 1$ for all n sufficiently large, since $| \sqrt{-1} | = 1$. Thus, $\sqrt{-1}$ would be a limit of units where these units cannot all belong to a finite dimensional subfield of k since any such field is complete, and, therefore, closed. This, together with our earlier remarks on the various residue class degrees enables us to assume that

$$\alpha_n = 1 + \sqrt[2^n]{2} \, \beta_n ,$$

where β_n is also a unit, so

$$1 + \sqrt[2^n]{2} \, \beta_n \to \sqrt{-1},$$

which is clearly impossible. Hence the degree of K over $\hat{k}$ is 2. Furthermore,

$$|\sqrt{-1}-1| = |2|^{1/2} < 1,$$

so $\varphi(\sqrt{-1}-1) = 0$, where φ is the associated place, and $\varphi(\sqrt{-1}) = \varphi(-1)$. Hence $f = 1$. Finally, for $\alpha \in K$, $\alpha = a + b\sqrt{-1}$, where $a, b \in \hat{k}$, and

$$|\alpha| = |a^2 + b^2|^{1/2} \in |\hat{k}|,$$

so $e = 1$.

Although $ef = n$ is no longer true if $|\ |$ is not discrete even if k is complete, it can be shown that in the complete case ef always divides n. We shall not be able to go into these matters here. The reader may consult Artin [1] for further considerations along these lines.

We observed earlier in (2.5) of this chapter, in the case of a finite separable extension, $K = k(\alpha)$ of degree n of k, that $n = \sum_{i=1}^{r} n_i$, where the n_i are the local degrees. Let $k(\alpha) \simeq k(\alpha') \subset \hat{k}(\alpha')$ be an embedding of $k(\alpha)$, where $\hat{k}(\alpha')$ is of degree n_i over $\hat{k}$, and α' a root of some $p_i(x)$ over $\hat{k}$ where the $p_i(x)$ are the irreducible factors over $\hat{k}$ of the irreducible polynomial satisfied by α over k. Since the residue class fields and value groups of k and $\hat{k}$ are the same, and since they are also the same for $k(\alpha')$ and $\hat{k}(\alpha')$, we have, in view of the previous theorem, that, if the valuation $|\ |$ on k is discrete, then

$$n = \sum_{r=1}^{r} e_i f_i,$$

where the e_i and f_i are the ramification indices and residue class degrees of the various extensions of $|\ |$ to K. We state this as a theorem.

Theorem 4.3. If K is a finite separable extension of degree n of k, and if $|\ |$ is a discrete valuation of k with r extensions to K

which have ramification indices $e_1, ..., e_r$ and residue class degrees $f_1, ..., f_r$, respectively, then

$$n = \sum_{i=1}^{r} e_i f_i.$$

Let us suppose now that K is a finite separable normal extension of degree n of k and that $|\ |$ is a discrete valuation of k. Then, if G is the Galois group of K over k, we have, in the notation of Theorem 2.4 of this chapter, that $G = \bigcup_{i=1}^{r} S\nu_i$ (disjoint), where r is the number of extensions of $|\ |$ to K. The local degrees, n_i, are the degrees of the $\nu_i(K)\,\hat{k}$ over $\hat{k}$, but $\nu_i(K) = K$, and, therefore,

$$e_1 = e_2 = \cdots = e_r = e,$$
$$f_1 = f_2 = \cdots = f_r = f.$$

However, by the previous theorem, $n = \sum_{i=1}^{r} e_i f_i$; whence, $n = efr$. Thus, we have shown:

Theorem 4.4. If K is a finite separable normal extension of degree n of k, and if $|\ |$ is a discrete valuation of k with r extensions to K, then all the ramification indices are equal to the same number e, and all the residue class degrees are equal to the same number f. Moreover, $n = efr$.

As a final consideration, we shall prove an extended version of the Eisenstein irreducibility criteria.

Theorem 4.5. Let $f(x) = x^m + a_{m-1}x^{m-1} + \cdots + a_1 x + a_0$ be a polynomial over a field k with a discrete valuation $|\ |$. If $|\pi|$ is the generator of $|k^*|$ with $|\pi| < 1$, and if $\pi \mid a_i$, $i = 0$, $1, ..., m - 1$, but $\pi^2 \nmid a_0$, then $f(x)$ is irreducible.

Proof. Let α be any root of $f(x)$, and consider $K = k(\alpha)$. Let n be the degree of K over k. Clearly, $n \leqslant m$. Assume that the valuation has been extended to K in some fashion and denote the extended valuation by $|\ |$ also. Now,

$$\alpha^m + a_{m-1}\alpha^{m-1} + \cdots + a_1\alpha + a_0 = 0$$

which implies that $|\alpha| < 1$, and, since we know that $\pi \mid a_i$, $i = 0, 1, ..., m - 1$ and $\pi^2 \nmid a_0$, we have that

$$|a_{m-1}\alpha^{m-1}|, ..., |a_1\alpha|$$

are all less than $|a_0|$. However, there must be at least two dominant terms in the equation, whence

$$|\alpha^m| = |a_0| = |\pi|,$$

or $|\alpha| = |\pi|^{1/m}$. Thus, the ramification index, e, of the extension is greater than are equal m. Hence,

$$m \geqslant n \geqslant e \geqslant m.$$

Therefore, $m = n = e$, the residue class degree of the extension must be 1. It is now also clear that f is irreducible, and the proof has been completed.

A special case of this situation was observed in Example 5 of the previous section. Extension fields, K, of k of degree n for which $e = n$ are called *fully ramified*.

Further extensions of Eisenstein's criteria are possible, where the valuation is no longer assumed discrete, but we refer the reader to the references for these considerations.

This concludes our discussion of matters centering around the extensions of valuations. Many important matters, such as the ramification theory of valuations, we have barely touched on or have not gone into at all. The interested reader is strongly recommended to consult the books and notes listed in the Bibliography, in particular, Artin [1], Bourbaki [5], Zariski and Samuel [23], and Schilling [19].

Appendix

1. Sets and Mappings

Let A be a set. If an element a belongs to A, we write $a \in A$. If a is not an element of A, we write $a \notin A$. Let $\{A_\alpha\}$ be a collection of sets where it is understood that α runs over some index set Λ. We denote the *union* of the sets by $\bigcup_\alpha A_\alpha$. This is the set of all elements which belong to at least one of the A_α. We denote the *intersection* of the sets by $\bigcap_\alpha A_\alpha$. This is the set consisting of those elements which belong to all the A_α.

Let A and B be two sets, the *difference set* (or the *complement* of B in A) is denoted by $A - B$, and consists of those elements in A which are not in B.

If the set A is contained the set B, i.e., if every element of A is an element of B, we say that A is a *subset* of B and write $A \subset B$, or $B \supset A$. If $A \subset B$ and $B \subset A$ we define the sets to be equal and write $A = B$.

The set consiting of no elements at all will be denoted by ø and is called the empty set or null set. We shall frequently use the notation for a set:

$$\{x \in S \mid P(x)\}.$$

This designates the set of all elements belonging to S which satisfy a certain condition or proposition, designated by $P(x)$.

If $x \in S$, the set consisting of just x will be denoted by $\{x\}$.

If A and B are two sets, the *cartesian product* $A \times B$, is the set of all pairs (a, b) where $a \in A$ and $b \in B$.

Let A and B be two sets. If to each element $a \in A$ a unique element $b \in B$ is associated, we say that there is a *mapping* or *function* f from A into B and write $f(a) = b$. We denote this by

$$f \colon\; A \to B, \quad \text{or} \quad A \xrightarrow{f} B.$$

If $a_1 \neq a_2$ implies $f(a_1) \neq f(a_2)$, then f is said to be *one-to-one*. If for each $b \in B$, there exists an element $a \in A$ such that $f(a) = b$, then f is called an *onto* mapping.

Let f be a mapping of A into B. Then, if $E \subset A$, the *image set* $f(E)$ is the set $\{f(x) \mid x \in E\}$. Let $F \subset B$, then the *pre-image* set $f^{-1}(F) = \{x \mid f(x) \in F\}$.

Next, if $f\colon A \to B$ and if $E \subset A$, the *restriction* of f to E is the mapping, denoted by $f|_E$, and given by $f|_E(x) = f(x)$ for all $x \in E$.

Finally, if

$$A \xrightarrow{f} B \xrightarrow{g} C,$$

then the *composite* map (or *product* map) gf maps A into C and is defined by $(gf)(x) = g(f(x))$.

Let S be a set and let $\sim$ designate a relation defined between pairs of elements of S such that, given any two elements a, $b \in S$, either $a \sim b$ (read a is equivalent to b) is true or false. The relation is called an *equivalence relation* if it satisfies the following conditions:

(1) $a \sim a$ for all $a \in S$ (reflexivity);

(2) $a \sim b$ implies $b \sim a$ (symmetry);

(3) $a \sim b$ and $b \sim c$ implies $a \sim c$ (transitivity).

A special equivalence relation is given by taking $S = Z$, the set of all integers, and defining $a \sim b$ if and only if $m/a - b$ (i.e., if and only if m divides $a - b$) where m is a fixed positive integer. This special equivalence relation is denoted by $a \equiv b$ (mod m), read a is congruent to b modulo m.

Suppose that S is a set and $\sim$ an equivalence relation defined on S. We denote by $\bar{a}$, the set of all elements of S equivalent to a. Such a set is called an *equivalence class*.

Theorem 1.1. If S is a set with an equivalence relation defined between pairs of elements of S, then S is decomposed into disjoint equivalence classes. We denote this by $S = \cup\ \bar{a}$. Here it is understood that the union is taken over only certain $a \in S$, so that the sets are disjoint.

Now, let $g\colon E \to F$. We define, for a, $b \in E$, $a \sim b$ if and only if $g(a) = g(b)$. It is clear that this is an equivalence relation on E.

Let $\bar{E}$ denote the set of all equivalence classes and consider the following mappings

$$E \xrightarrow{f} \bar{E} \xrightarrow{h} g(E) \xrightarrow{i} F,$$

where $f(a) = \bar{a}$, $h(\bar{a}) = g(a)$, and $i(g(a)) = g(a)$. f is an onto mapping. h is well defined and is one-to-one and onto, i is a one-to-one mapping called the *injection* map. Finally, $g = ihf$.

A set S is said to be *partially ordered* if there is a relation, denoted by $<$, defined between some pairs of elements a, b of S such that

(1) $a < b$ and $b < c \Rightarrow a < c$;

(2) $a < a$ for all $a \in S$;

(3) $a < b$ and $b < a \Rightarrow a = b$.

If S is partially ordered, and, if for every pair a, $b \in S$, $a < b$ or $b < a$, then S is called *totally ordered*.

Let S be a partially ordered set and let $E \subset S$. An element $b \in S$ is called an *upper bound* of E if $a < b$ for all $a \in E$. If $c \in S$ and if whenever $a \in S$, $c < a \Rightarrow c = a$, then c is said to be a *maximal element* of S.

A set S is called *inductively ordered* if S is partially ordered and any totally ordered subset has an upper bound in S.

The following set theoretical axiom, equivalent to the axiom of choice and many other set theoretical statements, will be assumed.

Zorn's Lemma.   A non-empty inductively ordered set S has a maximal element.

Applications of this axiom appear throughout the text.

2. Number Theory

As usual, we denote by Z the set of all integers. If an integer a divides an integer b, we denote this by a/b.

The *greatest common divisor* (g.c.d.) of two integers a and b is a positive integer d, denoted by (a, b), such that d/a and d/b, and, if c is any integer such that c/a and c/b, then c/d.

Theorem 2.1. The g.c.d., $d = (a, b)$, of any two integers a and b exists, is unique, and can be expressed in the form $d = xa + yb$, where x and y are integers.

If $(a, b) = 1$, then a and b are called *relatively prime*. The *least common multiple* (l.c.m.) of two integers a and b is a positive integer τ, denoted by $\{a, b\}$, such that a/τ and b/τ, and, if a/c and b/c, then τ/c.

The l.c.m. of any two integers a and b exists and is unique.

In Section 1 of the appendix, we introduced the equivalence relation $a \equiv b \pmod{m}$ in Z. The equivalence classes for this special equivalence relation are called *residue classes* (modulo m), and a set of elements, one from each class, is called a *complete residue system* (modulo m).

We denote by $\phi(m)$, the Euler ϕ-function, the number of positive integers less than or equal to m and relatively prime to m. If $n = \prod_{i=1}^{k} p_i^{\alpha_i}$, where the p_i are distinct primes, then

$$\phi(n) = n \prod_{i=1}^{k} \left(1 - \frac{1}{p_i}\right).$$

Theorem 2.2. (Euler's theorem). If $(a, m) = 1$, then $a^{\phi(m)} \equiv 1 \pmod{m}$.

Theorem 2.3. (Fermat's theorem). If p is a prime and if $(a, p) = 1$, then $a^{p-1} \equiv 1 \pmod{p}$.

Theorem 2.4. The linear congruence $ax \equiv b \pmod{m}$ has a solution if and only if d/b, where $d = (a, m)$. If d/b, then the congruence has d solutions modulo m.

Theorem 2.5. (Chinese remainder theorem). Given the system of congruences

$$x \equiv a_1 \pmod{m_1}$$
$$x \equiv a_2 \pmod{m_2}$$
$$\cdots\cdots\cdots\cdots\cdots\cdots$$
$$x \equiv a_n \pmod{m_n}$$

where $(m_i, m_j) = 1$ for $i \neq j$. There exists a unique solution of the system modulo

$$m_1 m_2 \cdots m_n .$$

Theorem 2.6. Let A denote a complete residue system modulo a prime p. Then for any $a \in Z$,

$$a \equiv a_0 + a_1 p + \cdots + a_{n-1} p^{n-1} \pmod{p^n}$$

where the $a_i \in A$. This representation is unique.

Consider now the quadratic congruence

$$x^2 \equiv a \pmod{p}$$

where p is a prime. An integer a, where $(a, p) = 1$, is called a *quadratic residue* modulo p if this equation has a solution. If a is not a quadratic residue modulo p, it is called a *quadratic nonresidue* modulo p.

If p is an odd prime, the number of quadratic residues modulo p is $(p-1)/2$, and, consequently, the number of quadratic nonresidues modulo p is also $(p-1)/2$.

For $(a, p) = 1$, the Legendre symbol, (a/p), is defined as follows:

$$\left(\frac{a}{p}\right) = \begin{cases} 1 & \text{if } a \text{ is a quadratic residue mod } p \\ -1 & \text{if } a \text{ is a quadratic nonresidue mod } p \end{cases}$$

We list the following properties of (a/p):

(1) $\left(\dfrac{1}{p}\right) = 1$.

(2) $a \equiv b \pmod{p}$, then $\left(\dfrac{a}{p}\right) = \left(\dfrac{b}{p}\right)$.

(3) $\left(\dfrac{ab}{p}\right) = \left(\dfrac{a}{p}\right)\left(\dfrac{b}{p}\right)$.

(4) $\left(\dfrac{a}{p}\right) \equiv a^{(p-1)/2} \pmod{p}$ if p is an odd prime.

(5) $\left(\dfrac{-1}{p}\right) = (-1)^{(p-1)/2}$ if p is an odd prime.

(6)   For an odd prime p, $\left(\dfrac{2}{p}\right) = \begin{cases} 1 & \text{if } p \equiv \pm 1 \pmod{8} \\ -1 & \text{if } p \equiv \pm 3 \pmod{8}. \end{cases}$

Finally, one has:

Theorem 2.7 (quadratic reciprocity law). If p and q are odd primes, then

$$\left(\frac{p}{q}\right)\left(\frac{q}{p}\right) = (-1)^{[(p-1)/2][(q-1)/2]}.$$

For proofs of the preceding statements, one may consult Niven and Zuckerman [16], Hardy and Wright [8], LeVeque [13].

3. Groups

Definition 3.1. A *group* is a set G together with an operation defined between pairs of elements a, $b \in G$ (we denote the operation by $a \cdot b$, or simply ab, and call it multiplication) which satisfies the following axioms:

(1)   For all $a, b \in G$, $ab \in G$ (closure).

(2) $a(bc) = (ab)\,c$ (associativity).

(3)   There exists an element $1 \in G$ (called the identity element) such that $a \cdot 1 = 1 \cdot a = a$ for all $a \in G$.

(4)   To each element $a \in G$, there exists an element $a^{-1} \in G$ (called the inverse element to a) such that $aa^{-1} = a^{-1}a = 1$.

A set G satisfying just the first two axioms is called a *semigroup*.

If G is a group and if for all a, $b \in G$, $ab = ba$, then G is called *commutative* or *abelian*. In this case, the operation is usually denoted by $+$, and one writes $a + b$ instead of ab. The identity is then written as 0, and the inverse of a as $-a$. Finally, one writes $a - b$ instead of $a + (-b)$.

Definition 3.2. A group G which contains only a finite number of elements is called a *finite* group. The order of such a group, denoted by ord G, is the number of elements of G.

Definition 3.3. A subset H of a group G is called a *subgroup* if

(1) $a, b \in H$ implies $ab \in H$;

(2) $1 \in H$;

(3) $a \in H$ implies $a^{-1} \in H$.

It follows from the associativity axiom for a group G that the associative law holds for any finite number of elements, and, if a_1, a_2, ..., a_n belong to G, we can write unambiguously, $a_1 a_2 \cdots a_n$. If all the $a_i = a$, we write a^n, or na in the additive case. If for some positive integer n, $a^n = 1$, then a is said to have *finite* order, and the smallest such positive integer n is called the *order* of a and is denoted by ord a.

Theorem 3.1. If a has finite order, and if $a^k = 1$, then ord $a \mid k$.

Let G be a group and H a subgroup of G. Define $a \sim b$ if and only if $a^{-1}b \in H$. It is readily seen that this is an equivalence relation and that $a \sim b$ if and only if $b \in aH$. Thus, the equivalence classes are the sets of the form aH, called *left cosets* of H. We have that either $aH = bH$, or aH and bH are disjoint. Furthermore,

$$G = \bigcup aH,$$

where the union is disjoint and taken over distinct left cosets.

One could proceed analogously be defining $a \sim b$ if and only if $ba^{-1} \in H$; one then gets a decomposition of G into *right cosets*, Ha.

Theorem 3.2. (Lagrange). The order of a subgroup H of a finite group G divides the order of G.

We write $[G : H] = \dfrac{\text{ord } G}{\text{ord } H}$ and call $[G : H]$ the index of H in G.

Theorem 3.3. The order of any element of a finite group G divides the order of G, and if ord $G = n$, then $a^n = 1$ for all $a \in G$.

Suppose there exists an element a belonging to the group G such that every $b \in G$ is of the form a^n, then G is called a *cyclic* group and a is said to be a *generator* of G. We write $G = [a]$.

If S_1 and S_2 are subsets of a group the product $S_1 S_2$ is the set of all elements of the form $a_1 a_2$ where $a_1 \in S_1$ and $a_2 \in S_2$. The associative law in G implies that $S_1(S_2 S_3) = (S_1 S_2) S_3$, where S_1, S_2, S_3 are three subsets of G. If S_1 consists of just a single element a, we write $a S_2$ instead of $S_1 S_2$. This is in agreement with our previous notation for left cosets. Clearly, if H is a subgroup of G, then $H^2 = H$.

Definition 3.4. A subgroup N of G is called *normal* if $a N a^{-1} = N$ for all $a \in G$.

In the case of an abelian group, it is clear that every subgroup is normal.

If N is a normal subgroup of G, and if aN and bN are any two left cosets, then

$$(aN)(bN) = abN^2 = abN.$$

Motivated by this, we consider the set G/N of all left cosets aN, $a \in G$, where N is a normal subgroup of G. It can be shown that the set G/N is a group, called the *factor* or *quotient* group, with respect to the operation of set multiplication, i.e.,

$$aN \cdot bN = (aN)(bN) = abN.$$

If G is a finite group, then ord $(G/N) = \dfrac{\text{ord } G}{\text{ord } N} = [G : N]$.

Definition 3.5. Let G and G' be two groups, and let $f: G \to G'$. f is called a *homomorphism of G into G'* if $f(ab) = f(a) f(b)$ for all a, $b \in G$. If f is also onto, then G' is called a *homomorphic image* of G. If f is a one-to-one homomorphism, it is called an *isomorphism*, and, if it is onto G', G' is called an isomorphic image of G, and we write $G' \simeq G$. An isomorphism of a group onto itself is called an *automorphism*.

An improtant example of a homomorphism is the following. Let G be a group and N a normal subgroup; map $G \to G/N$ by the mapping $a \to aN$ for all $a \in G$. This mapping is a homomorphism of G onto G/N and is called the *canonical homomorphism*.

If $f: G \to G'$ is a homomorphism, the set

$$K = \{a \in G \mid f(a) = 1'\},$$

where $1'$ is the identity of G' is readily seen to form a normal subgroup of G and is called the *kernel* of the homomorphism.

Theorem 3.4 (fundamental theorem of homomorphisms). If $f: G \to G'$ is a homomorphism of G onto G', then $G' \simeq G/K$, where K is the kernel of f.

Again, let G be a group and let H_1 and H_2 be two subgroups of G. Define for $a,\ b \in G$, $a \sim b$ if and only if $h_1 a h_2 = b$, where $h_1 \in H_1$ and $h_2 \in H_2$. This is easily seen to be an equivalence relation. The equivalence classes are sets of the form $H_1 a H_2$ and are called *double cosets* with respect to H_1 and H_2. We have

$$G = \bigcup H_1 a H_2 \qquad \text{(disjoint)}$$

where the union is taken over certain elements $a \in G$. If G is finite, unlike the case of cosets, distinct double cosets need not contain the same number of elements. One can show that the number of elements in $H_1 a H_2$ is given by

$$\frac{\operatorname{ord} H_2 \operatorname{ord} H_1}{\operatorname{ord}(H_2 \cap a^{-1}H_1 a)}$$

The following references are suggested for further considerations: Hall [7], Ledermann [12], Zassenhaus [24], Kurosh [11].

4. Rings, Ideals, and Fields

Definition 4.1. A set A together with two operations, denoted by $+$ and $\cdot$, defined between pairs of elements $a,\ b \in A$ is called a *commutative ring* if:

(1) A, with respect to the operation $+$, is an abelian group;

(2) A, with respect to the operation $\cdot$, is a semigroup;

(3) $ab = ba$ for all $a, b \in A$;

(4) $a(b + c) = ab + ac$ for all a, b, c in A (distributive law).

We shall in the future omit the word commutative, it being understood that all rings we consider are commutative.

A ring A is called a *ring with identity* if there exists an element $1 \in A$ such that $a \cdot 1 = a$ for all $a \in A$.

It follows immediately from item 4 in the definition of a ring that $a \cdot 0 = 0$ for all $a \in A$.

Definition 4.2. If A is a ring and if $ab = 0$ implies $a = 0$ or $b = 0$, then A is called an *integral domain*.

Definition 4.3. If A is a ring and if $A^* = A - \{0\}$ is an abelian group with respect to $\cdot$, then A is called a *field*.

An element a belonging to a ring A is called a *unit* if a has a multiplicative inverse in A.

Definition 4.4. If A is a ring, a subset I is called an *ideal* if:

(1) $a, b \in I$ implies $a - b \in I$;

(2) $a \in A$, $b \in I$ implies $ab \in I$.

If $a \in I$, an ideal, we frequently write $a \equiv 0 \pmod{I}$.

With respect to the operation $+$, condition 1 states that an ideal, I, is a subgroup of A, and, since A is an abelian group with respect to $+$, I is a normal subgroup, and we can consider the factor group A/I of all cosets $a + I$ where $a \in A$. A/I can be considered as a ring, called the *quotient ring*, by defining

$$(a_1 + I) \cdot (a_2 + I) = a_1 a_2 + I,$$

where $a_1, a_2 \in A$.

Definition 4.5. Let A and A' be two rings. A map $f: A \to A'$ is called a *homomorphism* if, for all $a, b \in A, f(a + b) = f(a) + f(b)$, and $f(ab) = f(a) f(b)$. If f is also one-to-one, it is called an isomorphism, and should f also be onto, A' is called an *isomorphic image* of A. We designate this by $A \simeq A'$. An isomorphism of a ring onto itself is called an *automorphism*.

Let $f: A \to A'$ be a homomorphism. The set

$$K = \{a \in A \mid f(a) = 0'\}$$

where $0'$ is the additive identity of A', is easily seen to be an ideal of A and is called the kernel of the homomorphism.

Analogous to the results on groups in the previous section, we have that the map

$$f : A \to A/I,$$

where I is an ideal of A, and where $f(a) = a + I$, is a homomorphism, which we call the *canonical* homomorphism. Also, if $g : A \to A'$ is a homomorphism of A onto A', then $A' \simeq A/K$, where K is the kernel.

If A is a ring with identity, then the set

$$(a) = aA = \{ab \mid b \in A\}$$

is an ideal containing a and is called the *principal ideal* generated by a. More generally, if S is a subset of A, where A has an identity, then the set

$$(S) = \left\{ \sum_i a_i b_i \mid a_i \in A,\, b_i \in S \right\},$$

where we consider only finite sums, is an ideal containing S and is called the ideal *generated* by S.

For the ring Z of integers, we have the following result.

Theorem 4.1. In the ring Z, every ideal is a principal ideal.

Another example of such a ring is the ring $F[x]$, of all polynomials in a transcendental element x over F with coefficients from the field F.

Definition 4.6. An ideal I in a ring A is called a *prime* ideal if A/I is an integral domain. An ideal I in a ring A is called *maximal* if $I \neq A$ and if J is an ideal such that $J \supset I$ (proper inclusion, i.e., $J \neq I$), then $J = A$.

One can show that given any ideal $\neq A$, where A is a ring with identity, there exists a maximal ideal containing it.

Theorem 4.2.   If A is a ring with identity and if M is a maximal ideal in A, then M is a prime ideal. Moreover, A/M is a field. Conversely, if A/M is a field, then M is a maximal ideal.

It is easy to see that a field, F, has no ideals other than F itself and $\{0\}$. This result implies that the only homomorphic images of a field are the trivial ones, where we map all elements into the additive identity, or are isomorphic images.

Let F be a field. Suppose $na = 0$ for some $a \in F$. Then, if b is any other element of F, $nb = 0$. One says that F has *characteristic* p if there exists a positive integer p such that $pa = 0$ for all $a \in F$, where p is the smallest positive integer with this property. If F does not have characteristic p, one says that F has *characteristic* 0. If F has characteristic p, then it is easy to see that p must be a prime.

Again, suppose that F is a field. The intersection of all subfields of F is clearly a subfield, F_0, of F and is called the *prime field* of F. One can prove that the prime field F_0 of any field F is either isomorphic to Q or to $Z/(p)$ for some prime p.

5. Glossary for Rings and Fields

In this section, we shall just list some definitions concerning rings and fields for handy reference for the reader.

Rings

1. Let A be a commutative ring with identity. If $a, b \in A$, then $b \neq 0$ *divides* a, written b/a, if there exists an element $c \in A$ such that $a = bc$. If a/b, and b/a, a and b are called *associates*. An element $a \in A$ is called a *prime* (or an *irreducible* element) if b/a implies that b is a unit of A or b is an associate of a.

2. Let A be a ring contained in a field F, and $S \neq \varnothing$, a subset of A such that $0 \notin S$. The set

$$\left\{ \frac{a}{b} \,\middle|\, a \in A,\, b \in S \right\}$$

is a ring, called the *quotient ring* of A by S, which contains A and in which all elements of S have inverses.

3. If A is a (commutative) integral domain with identity in which every ideal is principal, A is called a *principal ideal domain*.

4. A (commutative) integral domain with identity in which every non-unit and non-zero element can be written uniquely as a product of primes except for order and multiplication by units is called a *unique factorization domain*.

5. Let A be a (commutative) integral domain with identity. Suppose there exists a function $\delta: A \to Z$ such that for a, $b \in A$

(a) $\delta(a) \geqslant 0$ and $= 0$ if and only if $a = 0$;

(b) $\delta(ab) = \delta(a) \delta(b)$;

(c) if $b \neq 0$, there exist elements q, r in A such that $a = bq + r$, where $\delta(r) < \delta(b)$.

Then A is called a *euclidean domain*.

Fields

1. If K is a field and if k is a subfield of K, then K is called an *extension field* of k.

2. Let K be an extension field of k. Then K can be viewed as a vector space over k. If K is finite-dimensional over k, then K is called a *finite extension* of k. The dimension of K over k is also called the *degree* of K over k.

3. If K is an extension field of k, and if $\alpha \in K$ satisfies a polynomial equation $f(x) = 0$ with coefficients in k, then α is called *algebraic* over k; otherwise, α is called *transcendental* over k. The extension K is called *algebraic* over k if every element of K is algebraic over k.

4. An extension field K of k is called *normal* if it is algebraic over k and if every irreducible polynomial in $k[x]$ which has a root in K, factors into linear factors in $K[x]$.

5. Let $\alpha \in K$, an extension field of k. If α satisfies an irreducible polynomial $f(x) \in k[x]$, then α is called *inseparable* over k if $f'(\alpha) = 0$; otherwise, α is called *separable* over k. An algebraic extension field K of k is called *separable* if every $\alpha \in K$ is separable over k; otherwise, K is called an *inseparable* extension of k.

6. Let K be an extension field of a field k of characteristic p.

An element $\alpha \in K$ is called *purely inseparable* over k if $\alpha^{p^e} \in k$ for some integer $e \geq 0$. If every element of K is purely inseparable over k, then K is called a *purely inseparable* extension of k.

7. If K is a finite extension field of k, the set of all elements of K algebraic over k form a subfield, K_1. The degree of K over K_1 is a power, p^f, of the characteristic p of k and is called the *degree of inseparability* of K over k. The degree of K_1 over k is called the *degree of separability* of K over k.

8. If K is an extension field of k, and if S is a subset of K, then the intersection of all subfields of K which contain S and k is a field, called the field *generated* by S in K over k.

9. Let $f(x)$ be a polynomial with coefficients in a field k. A *splitting field* of $f(x)$ over k is an extension field K such that $f(x)$ decomposes into linear factors in $K[x]$ and such that K is generated over k by the roots of $f(x)$ in K.

10. If K is an extension field of k, and if $\alpha \in K$ and α algebraic over k implies $\alpha \in k$, then k is called *algebraically closed* in K.

11. If K is an extension field of k, then K is called an *algebraic closure* of k provided K is an algebraic extension of k, and K is *algebraically closed*, i.e., K has no proper algebraic extensions.

12. If K is a finite normal extension of k, the group of automorphisms of K which leave k fixed (elementwise) is called the *Galois group* of K over k.

13. Let K be a finite separable extension field of k and let E be the least separable normal extension field of k containing K. If G is the Galois group of E over k and if H is the subgroup of G leaving K fixed, write $G = \bigcup_i \sigma_i H$ (disjoint). Define for $\alpha \in K$, the *norm*, $N_{K/k}(\alpha)$, from K to k of α and the trace, $S_{K/k}(\alpha)$, as follows:

$$N_{K_{|k}}(\alpha) = \prod_i \sigma_i(\alpha),$$

$$S_{K_{|k}}(\alpha) = \sum_i \sigma_i(\alpha).$$

If K is a finite inseparable extension of k, let p^f be its degree of inseparability. Then define

$$N_{K|_k}(\alpha) = \prod_{i=1}^{n_0} \sigma_i(\alpha)^{pf},$$

$$S_{K|_k}(\alpha) = pf \sum_{i=1}^{n_0} \sigma_i(\alpha) = 0,$$

where the σ_i run over the distinct isomorphisms of K (leaving k fixed) into the least normal extension of k containing K.

For references see Van der Waerden [21], Zariski and Samuel [23], Jacobson [10], and Artin [2].

6. Adèles and Idèles

This final section is not a review section as the preceding ones. We just want to define some notions here in a rather special setting. We shall not go beyond a few definitions. However, because of the importance of these notions in such areas as class field theory and algebraic geometry, we feel that some introductory mention of them should be made. For a more general framework, as well as for applications, one may consult Artin [1], Artin-Tate [4], Weil [22], and Chevalley [6].

We shall denote by $S = \{|\ |_p\}$ a set containing all inequivalent p-adic valuations as well as the usual absolute value, which we denote here by $|\ |_\infty$, $p = \infty$. We now form the cartesian product $\Pi_p Q_p$ of the sets Q_p, where Q_∞ denotes R. Elements of this product are of the form

$$x = (..., a_p, ...)$$

where $a_p \in Q_p$. This set can be made into a ring by adding two such elements componentwise and by multiplying them componentwise also. The field Q itself can be mapped isomorphically into this ring by the mapping

$$a \to (a, a, ...) \tag{6.1}$$

where $a \in Q$.

We now consider the subring A_Q consisting of those x with $|a_p|_p \leqslant 1$ for all but a finite number of p. A_Q is clearly a subring which is called the *adèle ring* of Q. The elements of A_Q are called *adèles* or *valuation vectors* of Q. Certainly, for any $a \in Q$, $|a|_p \leqslant 1$ for all but a finite number of p, so A_Q contains the isomorphic image of Q under (6.1).

Next, we define for any $x \in \Pi_p Q_p$

$$|x|_p = |a_p|_p.$$

Thus, $x \in A_Q$ if and only if $|x|_p \leqslant 1$ for all but a finite number of p.

We consider the set I of all $x \in A_Q$ such that $|x|_p \neq 0$ for all p, and $|x|_p = 1$ for all but a finite number of p. I is easily seen to form a multiplicative group, and the elements of I are called *idèles* of Q. If $a \in Q^*$, then $|a|_p \neq 0$ for any prime and $|a|_p = 1$ for all but a finite number of p, so I contains an isomorphic image of Q^* under the map (6.1).

We finally note that a topology may be introduced in A_Q by taking a neighborhood basis of $0 \in A_Q$ to consist of all sets

$$P_x = \{y \in A_Q \mid |y|_p \leqslant |x|_p\}$$

where $x \in I$.

Bibliography

1. ARTIN, E., Algebraic Numbers and Functions (lecture notes), Princeton, 1951.
2. ARTIN, E., Galois Theory, Notre Dame, 1948.
3. ARTIN, E., Elements of Algebraic Geometry (lecture notes), New York University, 1955.
4. ARTIN, E., and TATE, J., Class Field Theory (lecture notes), Princeton, 1951-1952.
5. BOURBAKI, N., "Algèbre Commutative." Hermann, Paris, 1961.
6. CHEVALLEY, C., Class Field Theory, Nagoya University, 1953-1954.
7. HALL, M., "The Theory of Groups." Macmillan, New York, 1959.
8. HARDY, G., and WRIGHT, E., "An Introduction to the Theory of Numbers." Oxford Univ. Press, London and New York, 1954.
9. HILLE, E., and PHILLIPS, R., "Functional Analysis and Semi-Groups," Amer. Math. Soc. Colloquium Publications, 1957.

10. JACOBSON, N., "Lectures in Abstract Algebra," Vol. 1. Van Nostrand, Princeton, New Jersey, 1951.
11. KUROSH, A., "The Theory of Groups" (2 volumes). Chelsea, New York, 1955.
12. LEDERMANN, W., "The Theory of Finite Groups." Oliver & Boyd, Edinburgh and London, 1953.
13. LEVEQUE, W., "Topics in Number Theory" (2 volumes). Addison-Wesley, Reading, Massachusetts, 1956.
14. LORCH, E., "Spectral Theory." Oxford Univ. Press, London and New York, 1962.
15. NAIMARK, M., "Normed Rings," Noordhoff, Groningen, 1959.
16. NIVEN, I., and ZUCKERMAN, H., "An Introduction to the Theory of Numbers." Wiley, New York, 1960.
17. OSTROWSKI, A., Über einige Lösungen der Funktionalgleichung $\varphi(x)\varphi(y) = \varphi(xy)$. *Acta. math.* **41** (1918), 271-284.
18. ROQUETTE, P., On the prolongation of valuations. *Trans. Amer. Math. Soc.* **88** (1958), 42-57.
19. SCHILLING, O., "The Theory of Valuations," Mathematical Surveys, American Mathematical Society, 1950.
20. TORNHEIM, L., Normed fields over the real and complex numbers. *Michigan Math. J.* 1 (1952), 61-69.
21. VAN DER WAERDEN, B., "Modern Algebra." Ungar, New York, 1949.
22. WEIL, A., Adèles and Algebraic Groups (lecture notes), Princeton, 1961.
23. ZARISKI, O., and SAMUEL, P., "Commutative Algebra" (2 volumes). Van Nostrand, Princeton, New Jersey, 1958.
24. ZASSENHAUS, H., "The Theory of Groups." Chelsea, New York, 1958.

Index

Absolute convergence, 98
Adèles, 167
Algebraic
  closure, 166
  integer, 89
Analyticity, 114
Approximation theorem, 21
Archimedian ordered group, 78
Associated place, 69
Associated valuation, 74
Associated valuation ring, 68, 73

Banach algebra, 111
Banach space, 94
Binomial series, 51
Bounded linear functional, 100

Canonical homomorphism, 160, 163
Cauchy sequence, 16, 94
Characteristic, 164
Chinese Remainder Theorem, 22, 156
Commutative normed algebra, 111
Complete
  field, 24
  residue system, 156
Completion of a field, 26–33
Congruence, 26
Conjugate embeddings, 130
Convergence
  absolute, 98
  p-adic valuation, 4
  rank one valuation, 24
Convex functional, 103

Degree
  extension, 165
  of separability, 166
Discrete valuation, 143

Discriminant, 142
Divisibility, 164
Domain of convergence, 43
Double coset, 161

Eisenstein criteria, 151
Equivalent
  norms, 94
  places, 70
  valuations, 16
Euclidean domain, 165
Euler
  φ-function, 156
  theorem, 156
Exponential series, 46, 47
Extension
  algebraic, 165
  field, 165
  finite, 165
  normal, 165
  separable, 165
  theorem, 83–88
  transcendental, 165
Extension of a valuation
  archimedian, 126–128
  non-archimedian, 117–126

Fermat's theorem, 156
Fully ramified extension, 152

Gelfand theorem, 116
Global
  degree, 132–133
  norm, 136
  trace, 136
Greatest common divisor (G.C.D.), 155–156
Group
  Galois, 166
  ordered, 70
Group of units, 23, 67

Hahn-Banach theorem, 103, 106, 107

Ideal, 163
Idèles, 168
Identity element, 111
Induced valuation, 130
Inductively ordered, 155
Integral
  closure, 89
  element, 88
Irreducible element, 164
Isolated subgroup, 77
Isometry, 26

Kernel, 161

Lagrange's theorem, 159
Least common multiple, 156
Legendre symbol, 157
Liouville's theorem, 114
Linear functional, 99, 100
  norm of, 101
Local
  degree, 133
  norm, 136
  trace, 136
Logarithmic series, 48, 49

Metric, 3, 4, 15, 93
Metric spaces, 3, 4, 15, 93

Neighborhood (spherical), 15
Newton's method, 52–57
Non-units, 65
Norm, 92, 166
Normalized p-adic valuation, 23
Normed algebra, 111
Normed linear space, 92
Null sequence, 16

Order isomorphism, 78
Ordered group, 70, 77
Ordinal, 45

p-adic
  integer, 37
  numbers, 33, 34
  numbers (canonical expansion of), 35
  valuation, 2
Place, 67–70
Power series in Q_p, 43
Prime, 164
Prime field, 164
Principal ideal domain, 165

Quadratic
  non-residue, 157
  reciprocity law, 158
  residue, 157

Radius of convergence (power series), 43, 98
Ramification index, 121
Rank
  of an ordered group, 77
  of a valuation, 77
Regular point, 113
Relatively prime, 156
Residue
  class degree, 121
  class field, 9, 67
  classes, 156
Roots of unity in Q_p, 61

Semigroup, 158
Spectrum, 113
Splitting field, 166
Subgroup, 158
  normal, 160
Sublinear functional, 103
Symmetric convex functional, 107

Trace, 167
Trivial valuation ring, 65

Ultra-metric inequality, 3, 4
Unique factorization domain, 165

Unit, 162
Units, Group of, 23, 67

Valuation
  associated, 74
  discrete, 143
  equivalent, 16, 75
  general, 72
  induced by an embedding, 130
  non-archimedian, 5, 72

normalized p-adic, 23
of algebraic number field, 137
of rank one, 5
p-adic, 2, 5
ring, 9, 65
trivial, 9
vector, 168

Zorn's lemma, 155